Italian Armored Vehicles of World War Two

By Nicola Pignato

Color by Don Greer and David Gebhardt

Illustrated by David Gebhardt and Darren Glenn

squadron/signal publications

Two *Semovente da 75/18* self-propelled guns advance during an Axis counterattack in Egypt's Western Desert in the Summer of 1942. The lead vehicle's crew added sandbags and spare track links to the front hull for additional protection against British shells. The *Semovente da 75/18* featured a 75MM howitzer mounted on a modified M 13-40 or M 14-41 medium tank hull. Italian and German forces pushed the British into Egypt in mid-1942, only to be stopped and thrown back at El Alamein.

ISBN 0-89747-475-9

If you have any photographs of aircraft, armor, soldiers or ships of any nation, particularly wartime snapshots, why not share them with us and help make Squadron/Signal's books all the more interesting and complete in the future. Any photograph sent to us will be copied and the original returned. The donor will be fully credited for any photos used. Please send them to:

Squadron/Signal Publications, Inc.
1115 Crowley Drive
Carrollton, TX 75011-5010

Если у вас есть фотографии самолетов, вооружения, солдат или кораблей любой страны, особенно, снимки времен войны, поделитесь с нами и помогите сделать новые книги издательства Эскадрон/Сигнал еще интереснее. Мы переснимем ваши фотографии и вернем оригиналы. Имена приславших снимки будут сопровождать все опубликованные фотографии. Пожалуйста, присылайте фотографии по адресу:

Squadron/Signal Publications, Inc.
1115 Crowley Drive
Carrollton, TX 75011-5010

軍用機、装甲車両、兵士、軍艦などの写真を所持しておられる方はいらっしゃいませんか？どの国のものでも結構です。作戦中に撮影されたものが特に良いのです。Squadron/Signal社の出版する刊行物において、このような写真は内容を一層充実し、興味深くすることができます。当方にお送り頂いた写真は、複写の後お返しいたします。出版物中に写真を使用した場合は、必ず提供者のお名前を明記させて頂きます。お写真は下記にご送付ください。

Squadron/Signal Publications, Inc.
1115 Crowley Drive
Carrollton, TX 75011-5010

Acknowledgements

A special thanks to:

My Wife, Maria

Major Filippo Cappellano, Cavalry, Italian Army

Major Howard R. Christie, Ordnance, US Army

Dr. Fabio Temeroli, *Repubblica di San Marino* (Republic of San Marino)

Dr. Antonio Rosati, Rome, Italy

Author's Note:

The fasces was an ancient Roman symbol of authority that was resurrected by the Italian fascists, who took their name from this emblem. A fasces consisted of an ax with rods bundled around the ax handle. This symbolized the power of the state, which was strengthened by the unity of the people.

Roman magistrates were proceeded by an orderly bearing a fasces, which symbolized the magistrates' power over the life and limb of their subjects.

Italian fascists used the fasces as their party symbol, much like the swastika in Nazi Germany. This insignia was used on Fascist Party banners and worn by party members; however, the fasces did not appear on *Regio Esercito* (Royal Italian Army) uniforms and insignia.

FS numbers were developed in the United States <u>after</u> World War Two and their use here is solely an approximation.

(Previous Page) A column of M 13-40 or M 14-41 tanks advance along a trail in North Africa in 1942. The lead tank's crew placed sandbags on the front superstructure. This was done to supplement the weak frontal armor against British anti-tank guns. Armor for both the M 13-40 and M 14-41 ranged in thickness from 14MM to 45MM. An L tank ammunition trailer lies abandoned along the track.

Introduction

By mid-1938, Italy – under its *Duce* (leader), Benito Mussolini – realized how obsolescent much of its military equipment was with the possibility of a new European war in the near future. On 29 July 1938, the *Regio Esercito* (Royal Italian Army) launched a rearmament program that was intended for completion within five years. This project required an extended period of peace for Italy to consolidate and improve its economy, complete pacification of its African empire, and to move strategic industrial plants to safer areas.

The Italians had learned some military lessons from their experiences in World War One and ongoing conflicts in her colonial possessions; however, armored forces were not decisive in those wars. Nevertheless, a new doctrine titled *La guerra di rapido corso* (The War of Rapid Course) was issued in 1938. This called for a vastly increased rate of mechanization in the *Regio Esercito*. The new manual *Impiego delle unità carriste* (On the Employment of Armored Units) was issued that same year. An early step towards this direction was undertaken in 1937, when the *Regio Esercito* transformed the single existing motorized brigade into an armored brigade. The cadre for a second armored brigade soon followed.

Each of these new brigades consisted of one tank regiment, which had one L (*Leggero*; Light) tank battalion and two M (*Medio*; Medium) tank battalions. A two-battalion regiment of truck-mounted *Bersaglieri* (light infantry) was also assigned to each armored brigade. Rounding out the brigade were two anti-tank companies equipped with twelve 47MM guns, one Anti-Aircraft (AA) company with six 20MM cannon, and one engineer company. Few of the 1347 L tanks required for these two brigades were available in 1938, while the M tank was still a prototype.

Italian authorities planned to produce 268 M tanks, 697 new L tanks (armed with turret-mounted 20MM cannon), and 48 armored cars in 1939. The *Regio Esercito* only ordered 100 M 11-39 tanks that year, requiring the Army to equip their armored brigades with obsolete Fiat 3000 (M 21 and 30) tanks. These were Italian versions of the French Renault FT-17 from World War One. A later order for 50 more M 11-39s was cancelled in late 1939 in favor of 400 improved M 13-40 tanks.

The *Regio Esercito* transformed its 1st and 2nd Armored Brigades into the 131st *Centauro* (Centaur) and 132nd *Ariete* (Ram) Armored Divisions, respectively, in 1939. The provisional Table of Organization and Equipment (TOE) issued that year called for each Armored Division to have a tank regiment of four battalions and a *Bersaglieri* regiment of three battalions: one on motorcycles, and the other two on trucks. This TOE also called for one anti-tank company with six 47MM guns, one artillery regiment with 24 motorized 75MM guns and twelve 20MM AA cannon, one engineer company, and supporting services. Three of the four armored battalions were to be equipped with a total of 184 M tanks, while the fourth battalion was to have P (*Pesante*; Heavy) tanks; however, P tank development did not begin until July of 1940.

Ansaldo delivered new M 11-39s to the *Ariete* Armored Division (AD) between the Summer of 1939 and the Spring of 1940. The *Centauro* AD and the 133rd *Littorio* (Fasces) AD (formed in September of 1939) did not receive their full complement of M tanks until 1941-42.

The *Regio Esercito* did not order the new M 13-40 medium tank from Ansaldo until 16 November 1939. The Army ordered L 6-40 light tanks from Fiat and armored cars from Ansaldo in March of 1940.

In early 1940, the *Centauro* AD was deployed to Albania, which Italian forces had invaded on 7 April 1939 and soon annexed to Italy. On 10 June 1940, Italy declared war on France and Britain and attacked across the Alps into southern France. Several L 3-33/35 light tanks saw brief combat during this brief campaign. The *Centauro* Division's L 3s were involved in the Italian invasion of Greece (from Albania) on 28 October 1940. A battalion of 37 M 13-40s was deployed to the Greek Front to reinforce the *Centauro* Division in November. There were few engagements between Italian and Greek tanks. This division participated in the Axis offensive against Greece in April of 1941. After Greece surrendered on 23 April, the *Centauro* was redeployed north to support the *Littorio* Division's attacks on Yugoslav forces. The latter unit was equipped with only 93 L tanks, 24 flame-thrower variants of L tanks, and 15 M 13-40s. The *Littorio* was soon returned to Italy for reequipment with more powerful tanks.

The *Ariete* AD was deployed to Tripoli, Libya in January of 1941 to reinforce *Maresciallo d'Italia* (Marshal) Rodolfo Graziani's troops. They had invaded Egypt in September of 1940, but the British drove

L 3-35 light tanks assigned to the 133rd *Littorio* Armored Division and their crews are lined up for inspection in northern Italy in June of 1940. Each L 3-35 (formerly CV 35) was crewed by two men, who wear the standard black leather helmets and overcoats for *Regio Esercito* (Royal Italian Army) armored vehicle crews. The three

Italian armored divisions at the beginning of World War Two (except the 132nd *Ariete*, which had only two M 11-39 battalions) were solely equipped with L 35s. Each armored battalion was assigned 61 L 35s and 16 CV 33 Lf flame-thrower vehicles. Several of the latter are parked in the background, hitched to their fuel trailers.

Two M 13-40 medium tanks assigned to the 132nd *Ariete* Armored Division roll over a stone berm in North Africa. Both forward hull hatches are opened on the near vehicle. The *Ariete* – Italy's most **famous armored division – was deployed to Africa in early 1941, when it incorporated the M 13-40-equipped VII (7th) Battalion.**

then back into Libya the following January. *Ariete*'s two battalions of M 11-39s and three battalions of M 13-40s were sent piecemeal to Libya, where seven battalions of L tanks were already in place. The *Ariete*'s task was to halt the British offensive in Libya, but the British defeated nearly all Italian tank units, which were scattered among the infantry instead of concentrated into a dedicated armored force.

In early 1941, the *Ariete* Armored Division's assets totaled 93 L 3-33/35s (with 20MM anti-tank rifles later replacing the 8MM machine guns), 24 L 3-33/35 Lf flame-thrower vehicles, and a battalion of 52 M 13-40s. The medium tanks arrived in Tripoli soon after the arrival of the *Deutsche Afrika Korps* (DAK; German Africa Corps) under *Generaloberst* (Colonel General) Erwin Rommel on 14 February 1941.

The *Ariete* and the other Italian armored divisions were partially reorganized by the end of 1941, due to a new TOE the *Regio Esercito* approved in August of that year. This TOE called for a headquarters with three armored cars and a Reconnaissance Armored Group of four squadrons. The latter group had 26 armored cars, 56 L 6-40 light tanks, and nine *Semovente da 47/32* tank destroyers. The Division also had a tank regiment of three battalions, with a total of 192 M 13-40 medium tanks. Four armored cars were assigned to the Division's *Bersaglieri* (light infantry) regiment, while the Armored Artillery Regiment was equipped with 30 *Semoventi da 75/18* and 13 armored command vehicles. Other artillery assets included 24 motorized 75MM field guns, 12 motorized 105MM field guns, eight 90/53 motor carriage AA guns, 34 20MM Breda AA cannon on cross country trucks, and an Anti-Tank Battalion of 19 *Semoventi da 47/32*. *Ariete* had a battalion of 40 AB 41 armored cars, which replaced the Anti-Tank Battalion and Reconnaissance Armored Group found in the other armored divisions.

The *Littorio* Armored Division was deployed to North Africa in the early Spring of 1942, reinforcing the *Ariete* AD. They combined with the DAK to defeat the British 8th Army at Gazala, Libya on 11 June

1942. This led to the fall of Tobruk, Libya ten days later, then the Axis forces drove towards Egypt. The battle of El Alamein, Egypt from 23 October to 4 November 1942 nearly destroyed both the *Ariete* and *Littorio* divisions, while remnants of these units slowly retreated west through Libya into Tunisia. Elements of the *Centauro* AD arrived in Tunisia during this retreat and achieved some success engaging Allied units until the Axis forces in North Africa were forced to surrender on 11 May 1943.

The Allied invasion of Sicily (Operation HUSKY) on 10 July 1943 resulted in few tank battles. The handful of Italian tank destroyer units – primarily equipped with *Semoventi da 47/32* and 24 *Semoventi da 90/53* – were ineffectually deployed. British and American forces secured Sicily on 17 August, then invaded mainland Italy on 3 September 1943 – the same day Italy signed an armistice with the Allies.

Token armored units – equipped with L 3-33/35 and L 6-40 light tanks – were assigned to the Italian 8th Army on the Russian Front. This force was effectively destroyed by a Soviet offensive along the Don River northwest of Stalingrad (now Volgograd, Russia) in late 1942 and early 1943. The small Armored Group in Sardinia did not see any action, but the mechanized battalions on the French Island of Corsica expelled the Germans after the 3 September 1943 Armistice. The Allies showed their gratitude by disarming the Italian troops.

Two reconstituted armored divisions were stationed near Rome by September of 1943. The 135th *Ariete II* Armored Division was at full strength, which included 45 M 15-42 medium tanks, 124 *Semovente da 75/18* assault guns, 42 *Semoventi da 75/32*, and 12 *Semoventi da 105/25*. Other equipment included 12 *Semoventi da 47/32*, 50 armored cars, and several modern motorized guns and howitzers. The incomplete *Centauro II* Armored Division was also deployed near the Italian capital. It was equipped with 45 Italian made and 36 German-supplied tanks, plus twelve German-built 88MM *Flak 37* anti-aircraft/anti-tank

Three crewmen perch on the upper hull of their *Semovente* (Self-Propelled) *da 75/18* (RₒEᴛₒ 4467) in Egypt's Western Desert in the Summer of 1942. *Semoventi* (plural of *Semovente*) began replacing M tanks in the armored battalions in 1942. The 75ᴍᴍ main gun was also supplied with hollow charge ammunition, which made this vehicle a tank destroyer rather than a self-propelled howitzer.

guns towed by 8 ᴍᴛ (8.8 ton) Krauss Maffei Sd.Kfz. 7 half-tracks. Both divisions had not completed their training when Italy surrendered and were surprised when the Germans swiftly disarmed these units. This same fate befell Italian armored units deployed on occupation duty in the Balkans.

The Italian armistice left the country divided, with the Allied Military Government (AMG) controlling southern Italy. The AMG did not allow the few surviving *Regio Esercito* armored units to become part of the Italian Co-Belligerent Forces. The Allies were compelled to re-equip five Italian divisions to supplement their own forces during the difficult campaign in late 1944.

This situation was different in northern Italy, where the pro-German *Esercito Nazionale Repubblicano* (ENR; National Republican Army) had only small armored units. The ENR was the ground force for the *Repubblica Sociale Italiana* (RSI; Italian Social Republic) that Mussolini established with Salo as its capital. The Germans seized 977 Armored Fighting Vehicles (AFVs) from the Italians after the Armistice. The ENI was left with a few L and M tanks, *Semovente da 47, 75*, and *105* assault guns, and armored cars. Italian firms were ordered to continue producing AFVs for German requirements.

Much has been written about the shortcomings of Italian tanks in the North African campaign. Initially, their crews displayed a lack of training, while their equipment was generally equivalent to their British counterparts. Italian armored units displayed signs of mastery, which were demonstrated during the Battle of Bir el Gubi, Libya on 24 November 1941. The *Ariete* Armored Division broke up an attack by the British 7th Armored Division, who lost nearly 80 tanks to the Italians. In mid-1942, the new *semovente* assault guns engaged approximately 40 new US-built Grant tanks at Bir Hakeim, Libya. The *semoventi* destroyed 20 of the British tanks and forced the remainder to retreat. The Italian armored troops' parity in equipment quality dimin-

ished as the North African campaign progressed, especially after the DAK's arrival in early 1941. Italian crews were no less aggressive than their German allies, but Italian armored vehicles were increasingly underpowered and outgunned by their Allied counterparts.

Successes like Bir el Gubi and Bir Hakeim were short lived, since the *Ariete* and *Littorio* divisions were mauled at the Battle of El Alamein, Egypt in the Fall of 1942. All Italian armored units fought well within the limitations of their equipment. By 1943, the 38 Italian light tank battalions and 22 medium tank battalions – each approximately 300 to 500 men strong – suffered a high casualty rate. The 9542 total casualties included 4382 killed, 3875 wounded, and 1285 missing. The *Celere* (fast cavalry and *Bersaglieri*), reconnaissance, and *semovente* units also found occasional successes, but were equally battered in combat.

Ten years after World War Two ended, German *Generalmajor* (Major General) F. W. von Mellenthin – a *Panzerarmee Afrika* staff officer – made a fair and accurate assessment of Italian armored warfare abilities:

> *"I have no sympathy with those who talk contemptuously about the Italian soldier, without pausing to consider the disadvantages under which he labored. The armament of the Italian army was below modern requirements: the tanks were too light and very unreliable from the technical point of view and the Italian wireless* [radio] *sets were quite unsuited to mobile warfare and could not function on the move. During the North African campaign Italian troops gave many proof of dash and courage; this applies particularly to those who came from the cavalry regiments."*

Von Mellenthin was right, in that Italian industry took far too long to improve the quality of their AFVs. On the occasions they succeeded, the new AFVs appeared too late and in too few numbers.

Italian Armored Vehicle Production 1940–1945

Italian Armored Fighting Vehicle (AFV) production was low throughout World War Two, compared to Germany and the main Allies: Britain, the United States, and the Soviet Union. The *Regio Esercito* had 1320 L tanks and 100 M tanks available in 1940. Fiat-SPA completed at least 400 L 6-40 light tanks, over 300 *Semoventi da 47/32*, and 110 Fiat 665 Armored Personnel Carriers (APCs) at Turin between 1940 and 1945. During this same period, Ansaldo's Genoa factory produced:

710 M 13-40s plus 30 command tanks

695 M 14-41s plus 34 command tanks

220 M 15-42s plus 45 command tanks (plus 28 and 41 respectively after the Armistice, 3 September 1943)

30 90/53 self propelled guns plus 15 command vehicles

60 M 13-40 *Semoventi da 75/18*

162 M 14-41 *Semoventi da 75/18*

103 M 15-42 *Semoventi da 75/18*

190 M 15-42 *Semoventi da 75/18* (plus 55 after the Armistice)

61 M 15-42 *Semoventi da 75/34* (plus 49 after the Armistice)

30 M 43 *Semoventi da 105/23* (plus 91 produced after the Armistice)

11 M 43 *Semoventi da 75/46* (all produced after the Armistice)

1 M 43 *Semovente da 75/34* (plus 29 produced after the Armistice)

1 P 40 tank (plus 100 produced after the Armistice)

624 AB 40-41 armored cars

200 modified L 35s (known in the Italian Army as the L 35 modified or L 38).

1 AB 43 armored car (plus 102, including some AB 41s produced after the Armistice)

1 *Lince* scout car (plus from 129 to 250, according to sources, produced after the Armistice)

150 S.37 APCs

8 *Littorine Blindate* (armored rail cars) (plus 8 produced after the Armistice).

In the Summer of 1943, Italy's War Production Ministry envisaged a monthly production of only 150 tanks and 70 armored cars in 1944.

Italian Armored Doctrine

In 1938, Italy formulated a doctrine of high-speed mobile warfare based on which mechanized and airborne weapons would be considered important components. The exploitation by motorized forces would follow the use of the maximum mass available; in effect, the *Blitzkrieg* (Lightning War) envisaged by the Germans.

Nevertheless, the new manual on the use of armored units, *Impiego delle unità carriste* – released by the end of 1938 – was incomplete. The tasks of the various tank units used to support infantry, *Celere* (fast), and motorized units and those that were part of the future armored division were clearly defined, but there was little space devoted to reconnaissance and to tank-versus-tank combat. Nothing was contained about self-propelled artillery, air cooperation, or the action of armored units against enemy armored forces.

The attack formations obviously depended on the terrain: the battalion generally operated in columns, with platoons in lines. Each company formed a wave; distances were to be increased in difficult terrain. Mopping up operations during deep penetration pauses were also considered.

During independent actions, the following tank roles were established: L (Light) tanks contributed to security when moving and deploying near the enemy and support in maintaining contact; M (Medium) tanks were employed for long-range maneuver action and support in engaging enemy forces; and P (Heavy) tanks reinforced the M tanks' actions.

Although the main features of the new tanks were provided, no data concerning new armored cars and *semovente* (self-propelled) artillery was given. The latter – still on the drawing board – were not considered at all.

Additionally, mechanization needed not only equipment and financing – themselves not a high priority until Italy entered World War Two on 10 June 1940 – it needed good commanders, training, and planning. These aspects were simply not available in quantity and could not be improvised.

The early defeats led to the issue of better equipment and a reorganization. Revised manuals were published both on the use of the armored division – provisional regulation (*Impiego della divisione corazzata - Norme Provvisorie*, 27 August 1941) and tank unit training (*Addestramento dei carristi* 22 October 1941).

Italian armor doctrine was now complete: the flaws in the previous Impiego had been corrected and an entry for desert warfare added. Other publications dealt more in depth with the reconnaissance units' employment already mentioned in the *Impiego* manual.

The new doctrine and equipment only postponed the inevitable; it was too late to modify narrow minds and outdated tank designs.

Various armored vehicles are gathered in the final assembly area of Ansaldo-Fossati's Genoa, Italy factory in 1942. These vehicles include M 14-41 tanks, *Semoventi da 75/18*, and AB 41 armored cars. Ansaldo began M tank mass production with the M 11-39 in July of 1939. The firm completed the bulk of Italy's armored vehicle production between 1940 and 1945. These armored vehicles are believed to be finished in overall *kaki sahariano* (Saharian Khaki, approximately FS 20260) for assignment to North Africa.

Italian Armored Fighting Vehicles

On 13 June 1940, Italian tanks were grouped into three categories according to their weight. These categories were: L (*Leggero*; Light), up to eight metric tons (MT) (8.8 tons); M (*Medio*; Medium), between eight and 15 MT (16.5 tons); and P (*Pesante*, Heavy), over 15 MT. The letter was followed by two figures – the weight and year of introduction. The weight designation was deleted entirely after 4 August 1942.

L 3-33 and L 3-35 Light Tanks

The L 3 tank was developed from the British Vickers Carden Lloyd Mk VI, which Italy had purchased in 1929. After a few prototypes, the CV 3 (*Carro Veloce*, fast tank, 3 MT/3.3 ton) was accepted in 1933 and issued to the mechanized cavalry in 1934.

The small, turretless vehicle was designated *Carro Veloce* 33 (later L 3-33) and was armed with one 6.5MM Fiat-Revelli Model 14 air-cooled aircraft machine gun. Its suspension consisted of two sprung bogie assemblies, one unsprung wheel, an adjustable idler wheel at the rear, and the drive sprocket at the front. The tracks had main and joining links with double guide horns.

The *Regio Esercito* soon ordered a second batch with a new standard armament of two 8MM Fiat Model 14/35 machine guns in a single mount. These vehicles also incorporated minor changes to the hull: a new right front visor, roller-type ports and an armored visor in the rear superstructure. The suspension was modified with a track tension idler separated from the rear idler.

A third, large order was placed for CV 33s when the Ethiopian campaign began in October of 1935. Simultaneously, early CV 33s were retrofitted with the heavier weapons. Flame-thrower and radio variants were also introduced and were combat proven in East Africa.

The flame-thrower variant, designated CV 33 Lf (*Lanciafiamme*; Flame-Thrower), replaced one of the two hull-mounted 8MM machine guns with a flame projector. This projector threw a stream approximately 40 M (131.2 feet) at a continuous rate for two minutes and 15 seconds. The stream was cut off and on at will and was generally operated for only a few seconds at a time.

The CV 33 Lf often towed a 500 L (132 gallon) fuel trailer, which consisted of a two-wheeled chassis with a tow bar. An armor-plated shell housed a rectangular light steel fuel tank. A semi-rotary hand pump mounted at the trailer's rear was used to refuel, de-fuel, and mix the fuel components for use. This pump was placed under a hinged cover. A second, larger engine-driven pump was mounted in the rear of the tank. This pump drew fuel from the trailer to the flame-thrower via one pipe, and returned unused fuel to the trailer via a second pipe. The projector employed

A *Carro Veloce* 33 pilot vehicle rolls down a rocky hill during its 1933 acceptance trials. This tank fell more properly within the tankette classification, with a weight of 3.4 MT (3.8 tons). Early CV 33s (later designated L 3-33s) were armed with one 6.5MM Fiat-Revelli Model 14 air-cooled aircraft machine gun.

One of the four CV 33 pilot vehicles rolls past several *Regio Esercito* officers in 1933. Ansaldo developed this vehicle from the Vickers Carden Lloyd Mk VI, a British tankette. This tank had its 6.5MM machine gun removed from its left hull mount. Small pistol ports on production CV 33s replaced side grills along the upper hull sides. Both headlights were later moved to the front superstructure. Stowage boxes were located behind the superstructure.

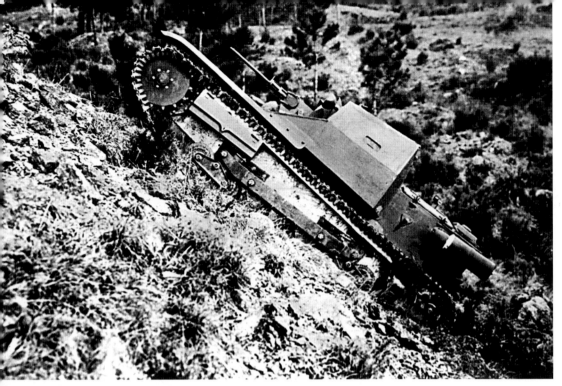

A CV 33 maneuvers through wooded terrain during the 1930s. These early tankettes were painted overall gray-green, which was the *Regio Esercito*'s standard vehicle color. Production CV 33s received a mottled two-tone finish, which usually consisted of dark green over brown. These colors were considered adequate for tanks intended to operate in northern Italy, where the Italians fought the bulk of their campaigns in World War One.

an engine powered electric ignition system to start and stop the flame-thrower.

By 1935-36, each CV company had a single CV 33 Lf platoon. The flame-thrower tanks proved effective against the Abyssinians (Ethiopians) in East Africa, but it saw little use in North Africa during World War Two. The CV 33 Lf – including a model deleting the trailer and mounting a 60 L (16 gallon) fuel tank over the engine – proved useful against partisans in the Balkans. The trailerless model was also studied for use by airborne units. Enough vehicles to equip a company were built, but they were then deployed to Yugoslavia for anti-partisan operations.

The basic CV 33 platform was also employed as a radio vehicle using the Marelli RF 3 CV radio, although its use in 1936 was limited to the company and battalion commanders. The improved Marelli RF 1 CA replaced the earlier RF 3 CV set during World War Two. RF 1 CA-equipped vehicles were employed as platoon command vehicles, but the diminutive CV 33 was considered too small to be effectively employed as a regimental level command vehicle. This task fell to the later and slightly larger L 6-40 CR (*Centro Radio*; Radio Center), which was equipped with RF 1 CA and RF 2 CA radios.

The new CV 35 variant introduced in 1935 featured a simplified superstructure made of bolted armor plates instead of riveted plates used on the earlier CV 33. A second batch had the side sliding flaps replaced by roller-type ports, while the roof access hatches were equipped with rectangular instead of circular vision ports. This vehicle was armed with two 8MM Breda Model 38 machine guns in the front hull. Bridgelayers and recovery CVs were also produced. The bridgelayers were capable of spanning a 6 M (20 foot) gap.

The conquest of Ethiopia, followed by the long, but victorious Spanish Civil War, made the small CV tanks famous around the world and beyond their actual merit. Several armies, including the Chinese, purchased them by the hundreds. In the meantime, the *Regio Esercito* had realized the CV's shortcomings, but since over 1000 vehicles were still available, the new turreted light tank was not given priority. Since a new vehicle was no longer under active consideration, the Army Staff decided to improve the existing CVs. The original two-part track links were replaced with monolink tracks traveling over a new torsion spring suspension system. The prototype also received a single 13.2MM Breda Model 31 heavy machine gun.

The modification's design and testing took a long time. A 47/32 tank destroyer prototype mounted on an L 3 hull was simultaneously designed and produced, but was soon dropped. The tankette had not been improved, nor was the new light tank in production by the Spring of 1940. It was not until mid-1942 that Ansaldo started modifying 200 tankettes with the new suspension, an episcope, and 8MM Breda Model 38 machine guns. The outbreak of hostilities in June of 1940 – sooner than the politicians had expected – forced Italy to fight in Libya with what the Army had on hand until July of 1940. The lightly armored L 3 was vulnerable to the .55 caliber (14MM) Boys anti-tank rifles mounted on British armored cars.

In the Fall of 1940, a few of these tankettes were rearmed with either the 20MM Solothurn S18-1000 or S18-1100 1100 anti-tank rifle or the 12.7MM Breda-SAFAT heavy machine gun. Other tankettes received 45MM Brixia infantry support mortars, while a number were also fitted with an anti-aircraft machine gun bracket.

In 1942 the remaining L 3s, initially designed for security reconnaissance duties, were confined to basic training and counter insurgency units in Italy and the occupied countries. After the Armistice of 3 September 1943, some L 3 tankettes remained in use with the RSI (Italian Social Republic), while the Germans seized other vehicles. A small number remained in both Italian Army and police service during the post-war years until 1952.

It is difficult to assess the L 3 series tankettes. Their small size provided good mobility and made them difficult to hit, but their dark and cramped interiors left little room for communications equipment. Starting the engine from inside the vehicle was extremely hard. The low height also offered poor vision. The suspension system was considered delicate. The two small roof hatches made escape difficult, especially if it overturned. The small size also affected the size of the fuel tank and subsequent range; the last tankettes in North Africa (mid-1941) had to carry external fuel in three 20 L (5.3 gallon) fuel cans ('jerrycans') arrayed across the glacis plate.

Fiat-Ansaldo L 3-33 (CV 33) Light Tank

Length:..................3.2 M (10 feet 6 inches)	
Width:....................1.4 M (4 feet 7.1 inches)	
Height:..................1.3 M (4 feet 3.2 inches)	
Combat Weight:....3200 KG (7055 pounds)	
Armor Thickness:.6MM to 13.5MM	
Powerplant:...........One 43 HP Fiat SPA CV3 four-cylinder, liquid-cooled, inline engine	
Armament:............Orignally, one 6.5MM Fiat-Revelli Model 14 machine gun with 3800 rounds in the hull; later, two 8MM Fiat Model 18/35 machine guns with 2240 rounds in the hull.	
Maximum Speed:..42 KMH (26 MPH)	
Maximum Range:..140 KM (87 miles)	
Crew:.....................Two	

(Above) The second CV 33 production series incorporated minor improvements and changes. These included adding an independent rear track tension idler wheel immediately ahead of the idler wheel. Two 8MM Fiat Model 14/35 machine guns replaced the single 6.5MM Fiat-Revelli Model 14 machine gun. These weapons were The tripod for a heavy machine gun folded and stowed atop the engine deck was a standard fitting for CV 33s.

(Right) Ansaldo equipped this second CV 33 for manufacturer's tests in the mid-1930s. Early tactical signs were painted on the superstructure sides. A new tactical markings system entered service in 1938; however, some vehicles retained the older markings early in World War Two.

A horizontal white bar painted on the superstructure sides identified a CV 33 assigned to a cavalry unit. A name in capital letters was usually painted above this bar, although this is not the case with this vehicle. This CV 33 was still armed with the single 6.5MM machine gun. CV 33s were were retrofitted with two 8MM weapons in 1935.

A small ammunition trailer is hitched to this CV 33. The trailer hauled additional ammunition for this vehicle's machine guns; however, the tankette's crew had to evacuate to a safe area in order to unload ammunition from this trailer. Units equipped with both CV 33s and later CV 35s (L 3-35s) were issued with these trailers.

The CV 33 *Carro Radio* (Radio Tank) for battalion and company commanders was equipped with the Marelli RF 3 CV radio set. A large loop-type antenna extended from the superstructure roof to the engine deck. Panniers for the radio batteries were located along the engine compartment sides. The CV 33 *Carro Radio* retained the two 8MM machine guns of standard, non-radio equipped CV 33s.

6.5MM Fiat-Revelli Model 14 Machine Gun

Barrel Length:	654MM (25.7 inches)
Feed:	50-round strip feed box
Muzzle Velocity:	640 M (2100 feet) per second
Rate of Fire:	500 rounds per minute (maximum); 450 rounds per minute (practical)
Rounds:	Ball

This early CV 33 was used to test the CV 33 Lf (*Lanciafiamme*; Flame-Thrower) vehicle. A long-barreled flame-thrower replaced the hull-mounted machine guns. The two-wheeled trailer held 500 L (132 gallons) of flame-thrower fuel, which was fed through a hose to the CV 33.

A CV 33 Lf spews flame during maneuvers in Italian Somaliland (part of present-day Somalia) in the Spring of 1936. A 60 L (16 gallon) fuel tank was mounted on the engine deck. This supplied flame thrower fuel when difficult terrain inhibited use of the 500 L fuel trailer. Markings on the hull side indicate this CV 33 Lf was the 12th tank of the 2nd Company, 3rd Platoon.

8MM Fiat Model 14/35 Machine Gun

Barrel Length:........	653MM (25.7 inches)
Feed:........................	50-round belt
Muzzle Velocity:.....	750 M (2461 feet) per second
Rate of Fire:............	600 rounds per minute (maximum); 450 rounds per minute (practical)
Maximum Range:...	5400 M (5906 yards)
Effective Range:.....	1000 M (1094 yards)
Rounds:..................	Ball and Armor-Piercing (AP)

8MM Breda Model 38 Machine Gun

Barrel Length:........	600MM (23.6 inches)
Feed:........................	24-round box magazine
Muzzle Velocity:.....	775 M (2543 feet) per second
Rate of Fire:............	450 rounds per minute
Maximum Range:...	5500 M (6015 yards)
Effective Range:.....	500 M (547 yards)
Rounds:..................	Ball and Armor-Piercing (AP)

A mixed formation of CV 33 gun-mounted tanks and flame-thrower vehicles prepare to attack across the North Africa desert. The CV 33 Lfs were deployed in columns, which allowed the next vehicle to continue in action when the lead tank was out of fuel. The Italians employed flame-thrower tanks in North Africa early in World War Two, particularly during the siege of Tobruk, Libya in 1942.

Both CV 33 crewman ride with the superstructure roof hatches open in North Africa. This tankette and the later CV 35 were crewed by a commander/gunner in the left hull and the driver to right. A towing eye is mounted on the lower front hull.

Exceptional agility was required for entering and exiting a CV 33/CV 35 tankette. Turning upside down in combat was nearly always fatal to its crew, since they could not get out of the vehicle without outside assistance. No escape hatches were fitted to the vehicle's undersurface. Italian armored vehicle crews usually wore dark blue overalls with black leather helmets.

11

(Left) Army officers demonstrate the CV 33 *Passerella* (Footbridge) bridgelayer to the *Duce* (Leader), Benito Mussolini (hands on both hips), during maneuvers in the Summer of 1936. This was the third most important CV 33 variant, after the standard machine gun and flame thrower variants. Mussolini served as a soldier on the Isonzo Front facing Austria-Hungary during World War One.

Regio Esercito Cap Badges

(Gold wire for officers, warrant officers, and non-commissioned officers; brass or black thread for other ranks)

Tanks   **Light Tanks**

(Bottom) The few CV 33 *Passerella* vehicles were assigned to units at Armored Brigade levels. The 7 м (23 feet) long bridge was stripped down into sections on a trailer towed by the CV 33 itself for travel. On arriving at the combat zone, this bridge was assembled on the tank's front. The crew laid the completed bridge over the obstacle from within the vehicle. A CV 33 *Passerella* crew took seven minutes to lay out this bridge.

The CV 35 entered production in 1936 and was the final CV variant. This vehicle was redesignated the L 3-35 in 1938. The newer tankette featured a simplified and bolted hull and superstructure, which replaced the earlier CV 33's riveted hull. This 1937 production model CV 35 had the same vision blocks that were introduced with the second CV 33 model. A shovel and iron bar replaced the tripod stowed atop the engine deck.

An L 3-35 Lf crew tests its flame-thrower at Langhirano, near Parma, Italy in 1941. The vehicle was assigned to the 2nd Battalion, 133rd *Littorio* Armored Division. The L 3-35 Lf's flame-thrower had a maximum range of 100 M (109 yards) under favorable weather conditions. High winds, rain, and snow reduced this range. The *Sottotenente* (2nd Lieutenant) standing to the right of the L 3-35 Lf wore the *Regio Esercito*'s M1940 gray-green field uniform, with a gold wire loop and bar on the cuff indicating his rank. (F. Cappellano)

An L 3-35 climbs up a rocky slope somewhere in the Balkans. The white vertical bar painted on the hull and superstructure indicated a tank assigned to a pro-German unit after the 1943 Armistice. The driver's hatch is open for greater visibility. L-3s could climb over 0.7 M (2 foot 3.6 inch) high vertical obstacles and cross a 1.45 M (4 foot 9.1 inch) wide trench. This tankette's 8MM machine gun had an elevation range of +15° to -12°, and it could be slewed 12° to left or right. Another L 3-35 and an L 6-40 light tank are parked on the road. (Bundesarchiv)

An L 3-35 Lf demonstrates a new flame-thrower near Rome in 1940. This vehicle tested a flame-thrower designed for mounting on turret-ed L tanks, including the L 6-40 light tank. Fuel was supplied from a 60 L (16 gallon) internal tank.

A new L 3-35 Lf with its flame-thrower tank mounted on the engine deck is slung beneath a Savoia-Marchetti SM.82 long-range transport/bomber. The Italians modified ten L 3-35 Lfs and several SM.82s for airlifting these tankettes to Italy's colonies in East and North Africa. Instead, the tankettes were deployed to fight partisans in Yugoslavia, while the aircraft supplied Italian forces in North Africa.

Three L 3-35 Lfs towing 500 L fuel trailers mount a simulated attack in Italy. Although such an attack was impressive looking, it was not highly effective against well-defended positions. Additionally, the unarmored fuel trailers were vulnerable to enemy fire.

This L 3-35 was modified with an improved suspension system in 1937. The suspension employed four large road wheels per side, instead of the six smaller wheels used on CV 33s/35s. Its armament was upgraded from two 8MM Breda Model 38 machine guns to one 13.2MM Breda Model 31 machine gun. Although this armament was successfully tested in 1937, the *Regio Esercito* only approved its fitting in 1941. Ansaldo modified 200 CV 33s and CV 35s with this new suspension in 1942-43; however, they retained the two 8MM Model 38 guns. This Breda weapon replaced the earlier 8MM Fiat Model 35 machine gun on Italian tankettes from 1939.

Italian armored crewmen stand near an L 3-35 in the Balkans. After Axis forces conquered Yugoslavia and Greece in the Spring of 1941, the tankettes were primarily used for anti-partisan operations. This vehicle is armed with the standard two 8MM Fiat Model 35 machine guns in the left forward hull. They wear the standard dark blue cloth overalls worn in or around their vehicles. The black leather helmets have soft leather neck flaps, which could be folded up. The two nearest crewmen each wear a gray leather pouch bandolier over the left shoulder. The crewman at the right holds the engine starting crank in his left hand.

Both crewman perch on the roof of their L 35 in the Western Desert in 1941. They are wearing black leather overcoats with the matching helmets. This vehicle was armed with two 8MM Breda Model 38s. This L 35 is painted overall Saharian Khaki (approximately FS20260), which was standard for Italian armored vehicles deployed to North Africa. Two *Regio Esercito* officers wearing cork sun helmets – and the arm of a third officer at left – lean against the tankette.

A pair of aft opening hatches were mounted on the L 3-35 fighting compartment roof. An aft-sliding plate in the left hatch roof allowed the commander/gunner to peer upward. The driver's right hatch was identical. This L 3-35 was painted overall Saharian Khaki for service in North Africa.

An L 3-35's driver uses a sextant while scanning the North African sky. L 3s generally lacked the roof-mounted anti-aircraft machine gun found on the M tanks; thus, they were vulnerable to strafing attacks. The vehicles' small size was their best defense against air attack. Each L 3 had large drive sprockets mounted at the front. Power from the aft-mounted engine was sent to the gearbox mounted in the front hull. In turn, power was transmitted to the sprockets, which turned the tracks.

An L 3-35 wades through a shallow stream during exercises in Italy. This vehicle could negotiate waters up to 0.7 м (2 feet 3.6 inches) deep driven by its tracks. L 3s were never employed on amphibious assaults, but crossed streams in the Balkans. Headlights for night travel are mounted on the forward superstructure corners. The narrow white bar on the hull side was part of the 1st Platoon insignia.

Leather covers protect the two 8мм machine guns on this L 3-35 operating in the Western Desert in 1941. Desert sand, churned when this vehicle drove through terrain, has coated the hull. The driver opened his hatch and poked his head outside the vehicle, while his commander/gunner remained 'buttoned up' inside the fighting compartment. The commander was provided with a periscope that was shielded by an armored vision flap. Slitted fabric covers placed over the headlights reduced the light emitted during night traveling. The circular device mounted under the machine gun barrels is the embossed metal *Regio Esercito* emblem that was common on Italian military vehicles. Cast in either bronze or aluminum, this badge featured the fasces, a five-point star, and RºEᵀº (*Regio Esercito*). Italian troops often removed this military badge after Benito Mussolini's fall from power on 25 July 1943.

Motor Vehicle Badge

L 3-35 Twin Machine Gun Mount

An L 3-35 drives up to an anti-tank obstacle – iron beams sunk into concrete – during exercises in Italy. This simple obstacle proved effective against L 3s. A 1 is painted over the 2nd Platoon insignia on the hull side. This new tactical sign type was tested in the 1937 Royal Italian Army Maneuvers in Sicily and approved in 1938.

Moveable Plate Covering Sighting Port

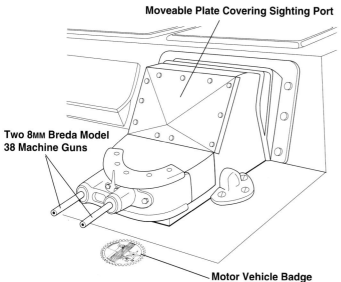

Two 8мм Breda Model 38 Machine Guns

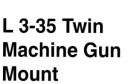

Motor Vehicle Badge

A motorcycle-riding British soldier rides past two disabled L 3-33s at Bardia, Libya in January of 1941. This port city near the Egyptian border fell during the British offensive (Operation COMPASS) against Italian forces in North Africa. The near vehicle was a second production series L 3-33 retrofitted with a 20MM *Fucile anticarro* cannon. This was the Swiss-developed Solothurn S18-1100 anti-tank rifle, which the *Regio Esercito* began purchasing in large numbers in 1940. It replaced one of the vehicle's two 8MM machine guns. The 20MM weapon penetrated up to 18MM of armor at 300 M (328 yards), which was effective against lightly armored vehicles.

One L 3-35 was modified into a prototype tank destroyer vehicle – the *Semovente da 47/32* – in 1939. The superstructure was removed and a 47MM Breda *Cannone da 47/32* M35 gun was mounted on the front hull. This Austrian-designed weapon was the *Regio Esercito*'s standard anti-tank gun throughout World War Two. The vehicle had a modified L 3-35 suspension and tracks. Although trials were conducted, the *Regio Esercito* did not accept the *Semovente da 47/32* for production.

20MM *Fucile anticarro* da 20MM 'S' Anti-Tank Rifle (Swiss Solothurn S18-1000/1100)

Barrel Length:	1420MM (55.9 inches)
Feed:	Ten-round Box
Muzzle Velocity:	910 M (2986 feet) per second
Rate of Fire:	15 to 20 rounds per minute
Armor Penetration:	40MM at 100 M (109 yards)
Rounds:	Armor-Piercing (AP)

A fixed metal shield was mounted in front of the gun to protect the *Semovente da 47/32*'s crew from enemy fire. It was dismounted for transport and placed along the engine compartment sides. A large slit in the center allowed the 47MM gun to elevate up to 56°. A smaller slit in the shield's left side allowed the crew to see targets. This vehicle is painted in a two-tone scheme, which is believed to be overall dark sand with streaks of red-brown and green. Fiat-Ansaldo usually painted their prototype and presentation vehicles in this scheme. A towing eye is mounted on the front plate, with the *Regio Esercito* motor vehicle insignia mounted on the left side.

Two early production L 3-35s are prepared for a mission in North Africa. These vehicles are equipped with 45MM Brixia mortars for infantry support. Each mortar was crewed by a gunner and a loader, which launched up to 18 rounds per minute. The Brixia weapon had a range of 530 M (580 yards). The near vehicle is marked with the sign for a platoon's 3rd Company.

An L 3-35 crewman walks away from a British Morris Model CS9/LAC armored car captured in the Western Desert in 1941. The near tankette is armed with 8MM machine guns, while a nearby L 3-35 has the 20MM Solothurn-designed *Fucile anticarro* anti-tank rifle. This weapon was effective against 'soft-skinned' and lightly armored vehicles such as the Morris Light Armored Car (LAC); however, it was ineffective against such heavier armored vehicles as the Matilda infantry tank.

Fiat-Ansaldo L 3-35 (CV 35) Light Tank

Length:...................3.2 M (10 feet 6 inches)
Width:...................1.4 M (4 feet 7.1 inches)
Height:...................1.3 M (4 feet 3.2 inches)
Combat Weight:....3270 KG (7209 pounds)
Armor Thickness:.6MM to 13.5MM
Powerplant:...........One 43 HP Fiat SPA CV3 four-cylinder, liquid-cooled, inline engine
Armament:............Two 8MM Breda Model 38 machine guns with 3200 rounds in the hull
Maximum Speed:..42 KMH (26 MPH)
Maximum Range:..120 KM (75 miles)
Crew:......................Two

An L 3 drives past the Napoleon Memorial at Ajaccio, Corsica in November of 1942. German forces occupied Vichy France and Italian troops took over the French island of Corsica after the Allied invasion of French North Africa (Operation TORCH) on 8 November 1942. This platoon commander's L 3 is equipped with a RF 1 CA radio. A whip antenna for this radio is mounted on the left upper hull. This RF 1 CA and antenna was the last modification made on L 3s.

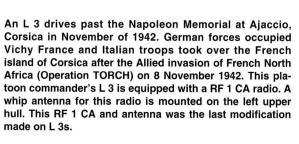

19

An L 3 with a new suspension climbs up to a dirt road in either Italy or Yugoslavia. The *Regio Esercito* had several L 3s remaining in service by 1 July 1943. They were employed on secondary duties, particularly in Italian-occupied Albania and Yugoslavia by that time. These duties included patrols against partisan forces that harried the occupation troops and pro-Axis residents. The thin armor and light armament prevented their employment against heavily armed Allied forces.

Tank Unit Organization

When Italy entered World War Two, there were two kinds of basic tank units: L and M tank battalions. While the L (light, i.e. tankette) battalion consisted of three companies, the M (medium) tank battalions were formed with two companies. Each regiment had three or four battalions, with two battalions equipped with L tanks and one or two with M tanks.

After July 1940, each of the three armored divisions had a single light tank regiment and no other armored vehicles. An M tank regiment was added in 1941, while the L tank regiments began to be disbanded in September of that year.

A 1939 L tank regiment consisted of:

– Regimental Headquarters (HQ)
– Staff Company
    One staff platoon
    One radio platoon
    One transport platoon.

An armored battalion consisted of:

– One Battalion Staff Company
    HQ platoon (One command tank, radio),
    Two to four companies, each consisting of one HQ platoon and three tank platoons,
    Flame-thrower tank platoons (each with four tanks for each company), and
    Replacement platoons (two tanks for each company).

The M tank battalion organization was similar except that flame-thrower tanks were not assigned to this battalion.

A reorganization was ordered in August of 1941. Each L and M tank regiment now consisted of:

– Regimental HQ
– Regimental Staff Company and reserve tanks
    One staff platoon (with radio workshop)
    One radio platoon
    One transport platoon
    Three reserve tank platoons (27 reserve tanks)

Three M tank battalions consisting each of:
    – One Staff Company
    – HQ platoon (Two HQ tanks, two radio center tanks)
    – Transport platoon
    – Repair platoon
    – Recovery platoon
    – Three platoons each of five tanks.
    – One Anti-Aircraft (AA) company equipped with eight 20MM cannon
    – One repair and recovery company, with heavy work shops

Heavy tank battalions were formed from 27 June 1943. Their organization was as follows:

– HQ (One P [heavy] tank, One command armored car)
– Three tank companies (39 P tanks and 18 ammunition carriers with trailers)
– Three recovery units (6 x 6 tractors with four axle trailers)
– Three workshops.

Several L 3s are refueled at Corni Lug, Yugoslavia (now Croatia) in August of 1942. They escorted an Italian convoy bound for Fiume, Italy (now Rijeka, Croatia). This and other Axis convoys were targets for attacks by Communist partisans led by Josip Broz Tito. Italy gave several L 3s to Croatia's pro-Axis regime, which employed the tankettes for internal security duties.

A crewman poses by the L 6-40 light tank prototype, giving an idea of the vehicle's size. Ansaldo originally intended this vehicle for export; however, in 1940, the *Regio Esercito* (Royal Italian Army) expressed interest in it. There were few changes between this prototype and production L 6-40s, which were delivered to the *Regio Esercito* from 1941.

L 6-40 Light Tank

In 1939, Fiat-Ansaldo agreed to produce a reconnaissance tank mounting a 20MM cannon and co-axial machine gun in a revolving turret. The vehicle was intended for export, but Italian military authorities examined it and were interested in its use by the *Regio Esercito* (Royal Italian Army). The Army originally ordered 583 L 6-40s from the SPA plant in Turin.

This order was soon reduced to 283 turreted vehicles; the remainder were to be converted into *Semovente da 47* light tank destroyers. Both orders were later increased. Fiat and Ansaldo also completed 30 turretless ammunition carriers for the *Semovente da 90/53* by the end of 1943.

The L 6-40 was powered by a 68 HP SPA 18 VT four-cylinder, liquid-cooled, inline engine mounted in the vehicle's rear. The power was transmitted via a drive shaft to a single disc plate dry clutch. From there, power went into a four-speed (and reverse) transmission that incorporated a dual range reduction gear. An epicyclical final drive and steering mechanism with front driving sprockets was used. Both the gearbox and final drive had a common oil circulation system.

The two double wheel assemblies were torsion bar sprung cantilever units mounted on supports fixed to the hull. The cantilevers of the two units were joined to hydraulic shock absorbers and slid, on the inner side, in a curved arm fixed to the tank hull. All bogie wheels and return rollers were mounted on roller bearings. Each track consisted of 88 cast steel links. Track tension was adjusted by an idler wheel with fork

device and torsion bar spring. The idler wheel also served as a road wheel.

The L 6-40 hull was constructed entirely of flat plates that were butt joined and either bolted or riveted over flat or angled metal strips. A bulkhead separated the hull into two compartments: the driving and fighting compartment, and the rear engine compartment. The driver's compartment housed the transmission and final drive assemblies, the driver's seat and controls, the batteries, and the radio equipment. The latter consisted of one RF 1 CA set, which was supplemented by a RF 2 CA in *Centro Radio* (Radio Central) command vehicles. A front louver could be opened in the glacis plate for cooling while two more air intakes were provided in the rear superstructure. The compartment roof accommodated the turret race (ring) and the driver's episcope over the rectangular vision port. A crew access door was mounted on the right hull side. The polygonal turret was offset to the left and incorporated two view slits in the sides, a roof mounted hatch, and commander's periscope. The turret rear had a removable plate to remove and service the guns and sighting telescope.

The engine compartment housed the engine, radiator and fan, and the fuel tanks. The engine deck had two access hatches with integral cooling air intake grills. Two additional air outlet grills were set further to the rear. The rear hull plate incorporated a circular plate for inspecting and servicing the cooling system. An L 6-40 Lf (*Lanciafiamme*; flamethrower) variant was also built, but it did not enter production.

The *Semovente* (Self-propelled) *da 47/32* was a turretless vehicle using a modified L 6-40 hull. Its open top superstructure was equipped

The L 6-40 was armed with a 20MM Breda Model 35 cannon and an 8MM Breda Model 38 machine gun in a revolving turret. Main gun elevation ranged from +20˚ to -12˚. Although Ansaldo designed the L 6-40, Fiat-SPA produced this vehicle and its derivatives at its Turin, Italy factories between 1941 and 1944.

At least seven L 6-40s go through an obstacle course during *Regio Esercito* acceptance trials in the Summer of 1941. This vehicle demonstrated a good cross-country performance in these trials. It was able to clear a 0.7 M (2 foot 3.6 inch) vertical obstacle and a 1.7 M (5 foot 6.9 inch) wide trench. The Italians deployed L 6-40s to replace the earlier L 3-33/35 tankettes in the reconnaissance role.

with a modified front plate mounting a limited traverse 47MM Breda 47/32 tank gun. The right access door, now deemed useless, was welded shut on early vehicles and deleted on later production *Semoventi da 47/32*. The open topped fighting compartment could be covered with a tarpaulin sliding on side bars to protect the crew and equipment from the elements. Platoon commanders' tank destroyers were fitted with a Marelli RF 1 CA radio set. Company commanders' vehicles were equipped with both the RF 1 CA and RF 2 CA radios, but deleted the main gun in favor of a dummy gun made of a metal tube that hid an 8MM Breda Model 38 machine gun.

The L 6-40's tactical employment was the same as in the L 3-33/35-equipped units. These new L tanks and tank destroyers were issued in 1942-43 to cavalry and *Bersaglieri* reconnaissance groups and saw action in Russia, North Africa, and the Balkans. The *Semovente da 47/32* equipped anti-tank battalions fought in Sicily and Corsica; the latter after the 1943 Armistice.

A number of L 6-40 light tanks were produced for German and RSI counter insurgency units in 1944. Some of these vehicles had modified superstructures and were fitted with a shielded 8MM Breda Model 38 machine gun for close defense.

Fiat-Ansaldo L 6-40 Light Tank

Length:...................3.8 M (12 feet 5.6 inches)
Width:.....................1.9 M (6 feet 2.8 inches)
Height:....................2 M (6 feet 6.7 inches)
Combat Weight:....6800 KG (14,991 pounds)
Armor Thickness:.6MM to 40MM
Powerplant:...........One 68 HP Fiat SPA 18 VT four-cylinder, liquid-cooled, inline engine
Armament:............One 20MM Breda Model 35 cannon with 296 rounds in turret and one 8MM Breda Model 38 machine gun with 1560 rounds co-axial with main gun.
Maximum Speed:..42 KMH (26 MPH)
Maximum Range:..200 KM (124 miles)
Crew:......................Two

An L 6-40 crosses a river while operating on the Russian Front in the Summer of 1942. This vehicle is the first tank assigned to the 3rd Platoon of an armored company. The tactical signs displayed on the front superstructure and turret side are larger than normal, while the individual number (1) is painted on the turret side ahead of the tactical sign. Fifty-six L 6s equipped the LXVII (67th) *Bersaglieri* Armored Battalion, which consisted of a headquarters unit and two companies of five platoons per company.

An L 6-40 is loaded in the bed of a Fiat 666NM truck, while a second L 6 is mounted on a trailer behind the truck. The L 6-40's combat weight was 6800 KG (14,991 pounds), or 6.8 MT (7.5 tons). This was over twice the 3200 KG (7055 pound) combat weight of an L 3-33. The Fiat 666NM (*Nafta Militare*; Diesel Military) entered service in 1939. This truck was 7.1 M (23 feet 3.5 inches) long, with a fully loaded weight of 6000 KG (13,228 pounds), and carried 5000 KG (11,023 pounds) of cargo or 20 men. The Fiat 666NM was powered by a 123 HP engine, which gave it a maximum speed of 48 KMH (30 MPH) and a range of 470 KM (292 miles).

This L 6-40 operated by the training school at Pinerolo had its 20MM main gun removed. A black 4 painted on the hull side hatch is the tank's only marking. The *Regio Esercito* approved the L 6-40 for service in March of 1940; however, production delays meant that it first entered service in mid-1941.

20MM Breda Model 35 Cannon

Barrel Length:.......1300MM (51.2 inches)
Feed:.....................Eight-round tray
Muzzle Velocity....830 M (2723 feet) per second
Rate of Fire:..........240 rounds per minute (maximum); 150 rounds per minute (practical)
Effective Range:..5500 M (6015 yards)
Rounds:................High Explosive (HE) and Armor-Piercing (AP)

An L 6-40 rolls over the Russian steppe in the Summer of 1942. Its crew smeared mud over the Saharian Khaki paint scheme to offer a more appropriate camouflage for the Russian Front. The L 6-40 was the heaviest armored vehicle deployed with the Italian 8th Army to the Russian Front's southern sector. Soviet forces routed the 8th Army between the Don and Donets rivers in southwestern Russia in late 1942.

Also Vidussoni, secretary of the *Partito Nazionale Fascist* (PNF; Fascist National Party) stands on an L 6-40 (R°E™ 3917) while addressing Italian troops in Russia in September of 1942. This vehicle was deployed to Russia in the original Saharian Khaki finish, which was later camouflaged with mud by its crews. The numeral 4 painted above the 3rd Platoon sign on the front superstructure is repeated on the turret side.

Experience in Russia prompted development of the Paghetti heating system. This diesel-fueled generator heated compressed air that was blown through four corrugated pipes through the upper radiator grills of four L 6-40 light tanks or *semoventi* (self-propelled guns) under the harsh Russian winter conditions. The Paghetti device weighted 353 KG (778 pounds).

An L 6-40 is parked on a causeway in Greece. This vehicle is believed to be painted in overall green-gray, with Saharian Khaki and red-brown streaks. White vertical bars painted on the front hull and superstructure side were a tactical emblem for this operation. The towing eye split the white vehicle registration plate on the front hull. R°E™ (*Regio Esercito*; Royal Italian Army) is in red on the left half (viewed from the front), while 5484 is black. This information was also displayed on a rear hull plate. A lion's head insignia is painted on the superstructure front, immediately below the turret.

This L 3-33 light tank was assigned to the 133rd *Littorio* Armored Division. The Division was stationed on Italy's western Alpine front in June of 1940. Hull side markings indicated this L 3-35 is the 1st tank of the 1st Platoon, 1st Company.

Armed with a 20MM Solothurn S18-1100 anti-tank rifle, this L 3-35 operated in Egypt's Western Desert in early 1941. The Italians designated this Swiss weapon as the 20MM *Fucile anticarro da 20MM 'S'*.

British forces captured this L 3-35 in early 1941 and repainted it in the Caunter camouflage scheme that was common on British armored vehicles in North Africa. This scheme was developed by Brigadier A.L. Caunter, who commanded the British 4th Armored Brigade in Egypt during 1940.

The 1st M (*Medio*; Medium) Tank Battalion operated this M 11-39. This unit participated in the capture of Sidi Barrani, Egypt on 16 September 1940. A white cross was painted on the turret rear for recognition by Italian forces.

This M 11-39 was assigned to the 332nd Tank Company in Italian Somaliland, Italian East Africa, in 1941. Brown streaks were painted over the gray-green base finish. A white band was painted around the turret.

L 6-40s and their crews are lined up for inspection in the southern French region of Provence in November of 1942. Axis forces reacted to the Anglo-American invasion of French North Africa by occupying Vichy France. These L 6-40s were assigned to a cavalry unit that performed reconnaissance duties. Standard unit markings are painted on the turret sides. Each L 6-40 had a two-man crew: the commander/gunner in the turret and the driver in the right front hull.

Ansaldo developed a *Lanciafiamme* (Flame-Thrower) variant of the L 6-40. The flame-thrower replaced the 20MM Breda Model 35 cannon in the turret; however, the coaxial 8MM Breda Model 38 machine gun was retained. This device was nearly identical to the flame-throwers mounted on L 3-33/35s. An unknown number of L 6-40 Lfs were built, but this variant did not enter service.

Fiat-Ansaldo *Semovente da 47/32* Assault Gun (on L 6-40 chassis)

Length:...................	3.8 M (12 feet 5.6 inches)
Width:....................	1.9 M (6 feet 2.8 inches)
Height:...................	1.7 M (5 feet 6.9 inches)
Combat Weight:....	6500 KG (14,330 pounds)
Armor Thickness:.	6MM to 30MM
Powerplant:...........	One 68 HP Fiat SPA 18 VT four-cylinder, liquid-cooled, inline engine
Armament:.............	One 47MM Ansaldo 47/32 gun with 70 rounds and one 8MM Breda Model 38 machine gun with 1608 rounds in the hull.
Maximum Speed:..	42 KMH (26 MPH)
Maximum Range:...	200 KM (124 miles)
Crew:......................	Three

The *Semovente da 47/32* mounted a 47MM Ansaldo 47/32 gun on a turretless L 6-40 chassis. This prototype had an armored roof, which was deleted on production vehicles. It was ordered into production in early 1941, but did not enter service until late 1942. By that date, it was ineffective against most Allied armored vehicles it faced on both the Russian and North African fronts.

The *Semovente da 47/32*'s three-man crew man their stations in the fighting compartment. The driver sat in the right front compartment section, with the loader immediately aft of him and the commander/gunner to left. The platoon commander's vehicle replaced the loader with a radio operator to handle the additional communications equipment.

Ansaldo produced several examples of a *Carro Commando* L 40 company command version of the *Semovente da 47/32*. It was similar to a standard *semovente*; however, the hull-mounted 47MM gun was replaced by a fake 47MM concealing an 8MM Breda Model 38 machine gun. Additional radio equipment was installed inside the fighting compartment. This equipment prevented use of the right side access door, which was soon eliminated during production.

The *Cingoletta* armored carrier variant of the *Semovente da 47/32* was proposed at the end of 1941. The vehicle was intended to tow ammunition trailers supplying the *semovente* units in combat. It was armed with a 13.2MM Breda Model 31 machine gun in the forward hull and an 8MM Breda Model 38 in the aft fighting compartment. The *Regio Esercito* was not interested in the *Cingoletta*, whose role was taken by unarmored AS 37 Saharian support vehicles.

13.2MM Breda Model 31 Machine Gun

Barrel Length:	1000MM (39.4 inches)
Feed:	12-round box
Muzzle Velocity:	790 M (2592 feet) per second
Rate of Fire:	500 rounds per minute (theoretical); 400 rounds per minute (practical)
Effective Range:	4000 M (4374 yards)
Rounds:	Armor-Piercing (AP)
Armor Penetration:	Not available

A company of *Semoventi da 47/32* attack Allied forces in Tunisia in early 1943. This image was taken from a motion picture describing this assault. A radio-equipped company commander's vehicle (nearest to camera) leads this attack. After the defeat of Axis forces in North Africa in 1943, *Semoventi da 47/32* were employed in Sicily and Corsica.

This L 6-40 light tank (R°E™ 4032) was assigned to the 14th *Alessandria* Cavalry Regiment in Albania in early 1943. This Regiment was part of the 1st *Eugenio di Savoia Celere* (Fast) Division.

The Commander of the XVII (17th) Tank Battalion rode in this L 6-40 (R°E™ 4050) in North Africa in 1942. The rectangular Battalion emblem on the turret sides and hull front was in red and light blue for the 1st and 2nd Companies, respectively.

This *Semovente da 47/32* was the 1st vehicle of the 1st Platoon, 1st Company. The *semovente* – a 47MM gun on a modified L 6-40 chassis – was based at Bastia, Corsica in November of 1942.

This overall gray-green M 13-40 was the 2nd tank of the 1st Platoon, 1st Company, IV (4th) Tank Battalion. The Battalion was part of the 134th Centauro Armored Division, which took part in the Italian invasion of Greece. This M 13-40 was destroyed at Monastir on 19 March 1941.

The 132nd *Ariete* Armored Division operated this *Semovente da 75/18* at El Alamein, Egypt in August of 1942. The overall Saharian Khaki vehicle displays the black and yellow inverted triangle marking assigned to many *semoventi*.

The *Ariete* Armored Division's black ram insignia is painted on the hull door of this M 14-41 medium tank. This Division spearheaded Italy's contribution to the Axis drive on Egypt in the Summer of 1942. A 70 CM (27.6 inch) white air recognition disc is painted on the turret roof.

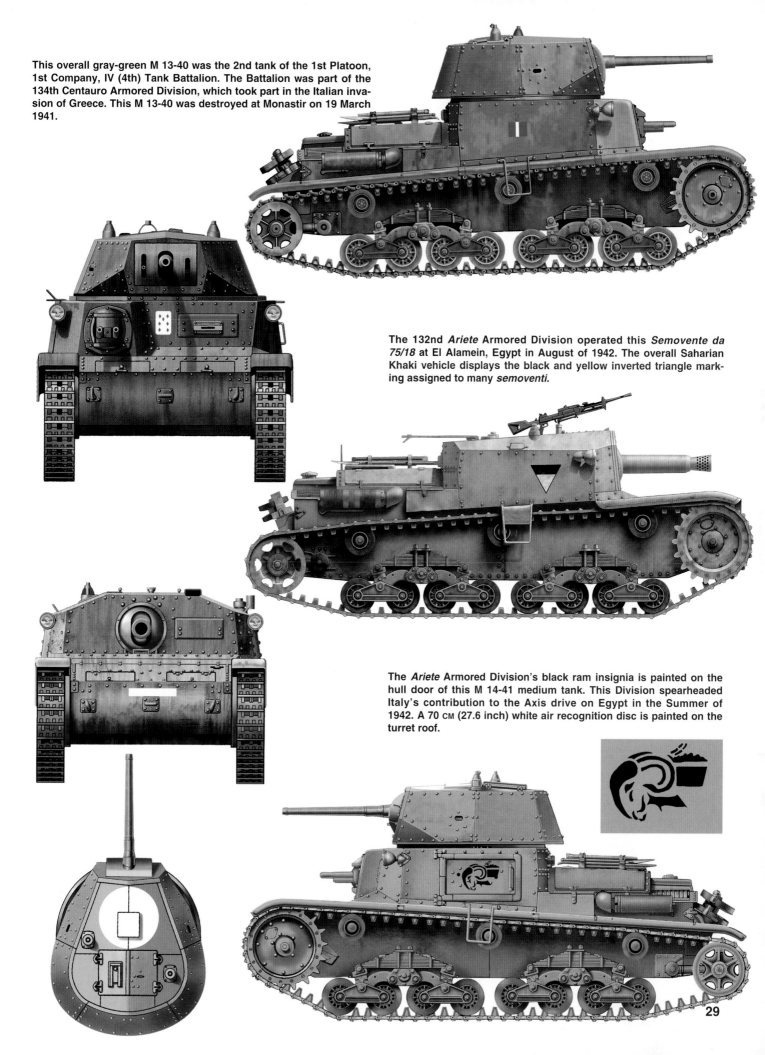

An M 11-39 pilot model moves through a country lane in the northern Italian region of Piedmont during *Regio Esercito* maneuvers in August of 1939. These early vehicles had larger headlights mounted on the superstructure sides than appeared on production M 11-39s. It was finished in a straight edged camouflage scheme of reddish brown and medium green. The M 11-39 was designed in 1936 as a 'breakthrough tank' for assaulting enemy formations.

M 11-39 Medium Tank

The M (*Medio*; Medium) tanks formed the bulk of Italy's armored force in World War Two. The M 11-39 was the first of the new M tanks to be fielded. Ansaldo produced 100 units in 1939-40.

The prototype tank was completed in 1937 and standardized in 1938, when it was shown to *il Duce* (The Leader), Benito Mussolini, during his visit to Genoa. The 3rd Tank Regiment in Bologna tested one company of M 11-39s during the 1939 war games.

The M 11-39 was of conventional design for the times and employed a crew of three: commander/machine gunner, gunner, and driver. Its armament consisted of a 37MM Vickers-Terni L/40 gun in the right front hull with a limited power traverse of 15° left and right. A small, circular, hand operated turret was offset to the left on the fighting compartment roof. This turret was equipped with two gimbal-mounted 8MM Breda Model 38 machine guns. A periscope was provided for the commander near the turret's hatch. Single vision slots were mounted on each side of the fighting compartment, while two were mounted at the rear. An RF 1 CA radio set was planned for each vehicle, but delayed deliveries of these radios meant that only the prototype was so equipped.

The driver was provided with an armored flap with an integral vision slit and a replaceable glass vision block. An episcope was fitted into the roof. Telescopic sights were provided for the weapons. The hull was equipped with a single access hatch on the left side and a roof mounted hatch on the right. Two hatches on the glacis plate provided access to the final drive components and transmission. These hatches could be partially opened by remote control from the driver's position to provide additional ventilation.

The M 11-39 hull was constructed using bolted armor plates ranging from 6MM to 30MM thick and capable of stopping 20MM fire. The vehicle was powered by a 125 HP SPA 8T eight-cylinder, liquid-cooled, inline diesel engine mounted in the rear hull.

Its suspension consisted of two eight-wheeled, articulated bogie assemblies on each hull side. Each bogie was equipped with standard laminated semi-elliptic springs. The drive sprocket was mounted at the front, while the adjustable idler wheels were at the rear. The drive sprockets broke tradition by having the final drive reduction gears inside the sprocket. This deleted the need for large final drive housings projecting forward of the nose. Three small return rollers supported the upper track run.

Production M 11-39s were only slightly different from the prototypes and the initial batch of vehicles. A second order was canceled, since a new version was ready in late 1939. This new development replaced the hull mounted, limited traverse main gun with a more powerful semi-automatic 47/32 gun in a revolving turret. The two 8MM machine guns were relocated to the right front superstructure. An 8MM machine gun was placed onto a bracket in front of the commander's hatches for anti-aircraft use. This model became the prototype of the improved M 13-40.

Two companies of M 11-39s were deployed to East Africa just before World War Two. Although they engaged British forces, the results were inconclusive. The remaining two M 11-39 battalions were sent to Libya in July of 1940 – just in time for the Italian advance to Sidi Barrani. Both battalions were destroyed in the British counter-offensive five months later. Some M 11-39s were recovered by the Australians and used in the attack on Tobruk.

The M 11-39 was not considered successful for several reasons. African conditions were not considered when the vehicle was designed and tested and its reliability suffered. Additionally, the M 11-39 lacked a dedicated transporter; the tank often had to drive from the African ports to the front, which further eroded its reliability. The hull-mounted main armament, limited armor protection, and the absence of radio equipment compromised its tactical value. Despite its shortcomings, the M 11-39 was important in the development of Italian Armored Fighting Vehicles (AFVs) of the period. It was the model from which all subsequent World War Two M and P (*Pesante*; Heavy) tanks originated.

Foreign military officers examine the pre-production M 11-39 that participated in *Regio Esercito* maneuvers in August of 1939. These exercises – held in northern Italy's Piedmont region – were the Royal Italian Army's last peacetime maneuvers. The front brake cooling hatches are opened on the glacis plate, while both the turret hatch and the gunner's hatch on the hull are closed.

A production M 11-39 moves over an obstacle during the crew training in the Spring of 1940. This vehicle was capable of moving over 0.8 M (2 foot 7.5 inch) high vertical obstacles and across 2.1 M (6 foot 10.7 inch) wide trenches. Production M 11-39s had shorter mudguards than the pilot vehicles and were finished in a soft-edged scheme of red brown with green bands.

The crew of this M 11-39 draped branches over their vehicle. This tank was assigned to the 332nd Company that was deployed in Italian East Africa in 1940. Small numbers of M 11-39s were deployed to Italy's colonies of Italian Somaliland (now part of Somalia), Eritrea, and Ethiopia (the latter conquered in 1935-36). Italian forces successfully attacked neighboring British Somaliland in August of 1940. British counteroffensives from January of 1941 resulted in the last Italian forces in East Africa surrendering on 27 November 1941.

M 11-39 Fighting Compartment

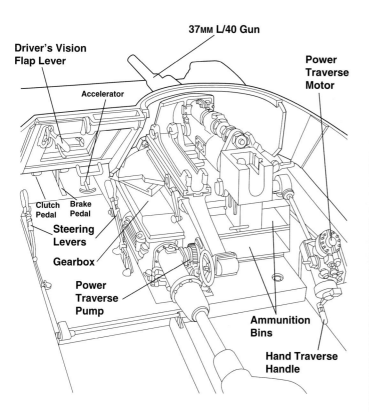

Driver's Vision Flap Lever

Accelerator

37MM L/40 Gun

Power Traverse Motor

Clutch Pedal

Brake Pedal

Steering Levers

Gearbox

Power Traverse Pump

Ammunition Bins

Hand Traverse Handle

US troops captured this *Semovente da 90/53* (R°E™ 5825) in Sicily in July of 1943. This vehicle was assigned to the CLXIII (163rd) Support Artillery Group. The Americans later sent this *semovente* to the Aberdeen Proving Ground, Maryland for evaluation and display.

The German Army operated this *Carro Commando da M 15-42* command vehicle at Corvara, Northern Italy in May of 1945. This vehicle used a modified M 15-42 medium tank hull, with additional radio equipment. It was armed with one 13.2MM Breda Model 31 machine gun in the forward hull.

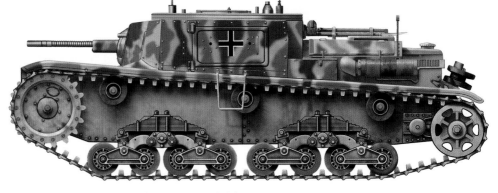

The Italian National Army's *Leoncello* (Little Lion) Cavalry Unit operated this *Semovente da 105/25* in North Italy during the Summer of 1944. This vehicle mounted a 105MM gun on a modified M 15-42 chassis. The Italians nicknamed the *Semovente da 105/25* the *Bassotto* (Dachshund).

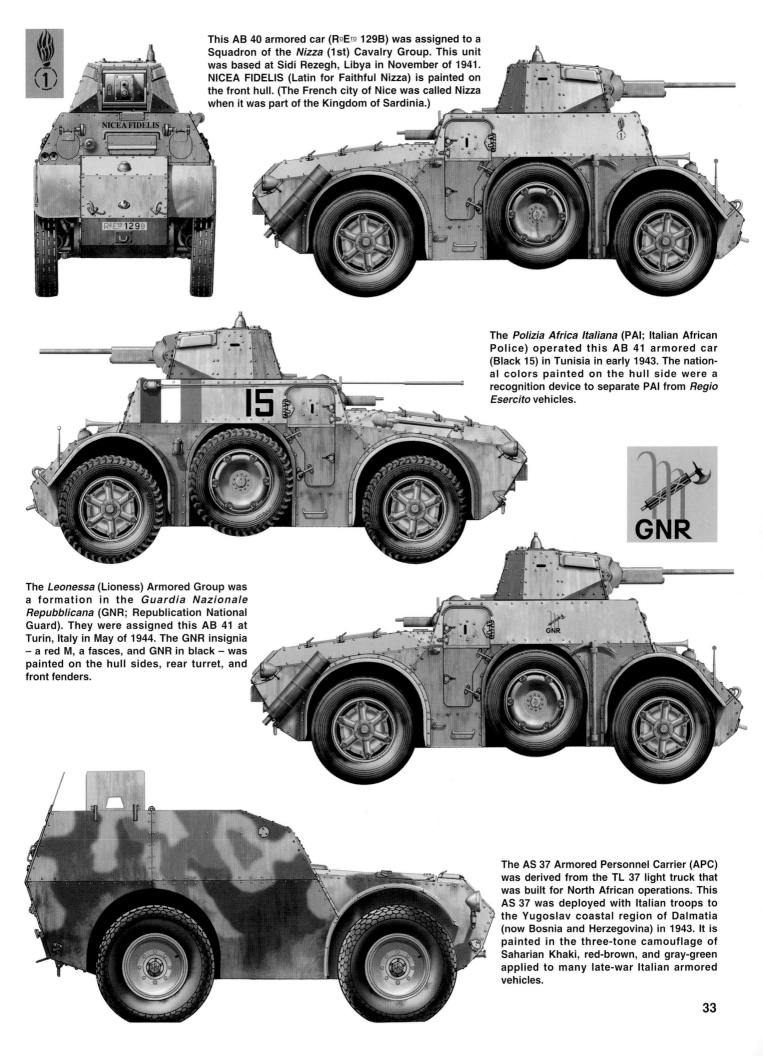

This AB 40 armored car (R°E᷾ᵀᴼ 129B) was assigned to a Squadron of the *Nizza* (1st) Cavalry Group. This unit was based at Sidi Rezegh, Libya in November of 1941. NICEA FIDELIS (Latin for Faithful Nizza) is painted on the front hull. (The French city of Nice was called Nizza when it was part of the Kingdom of Sardinia.)

NICEA FIDELIS

R°E᷾ᵀᴼ 129B

The *Polizia Africa Italiana* (PAI; Italian African Police) operated this AB 41 armored car (Black 15) in Tunisia in early 1943. The national colors painted on the hull side were a recognition device to separate PAI from *Regio Esercito* vehicles.

15

GNR

The *Leonessa* (Lioness) Armored Group was a formation in the *Guardia Nazionale Repubblicana* (GNR; Republication National Guard). They were assigned this AB 41 at Turin, Italy in May of 1944. The GNR insignia – a red M, a fasces, and GNR in black – was painted on the hull sides, rear turret, and front fenders.

GNR

The AS 37 Armored Personnel Carrier (APC) was derived from the TL 37 light truck that was built for North African operations. This AS 37 was deployed with Italian troops to the Yugoslav coastal region of Dalmatia (now Bosnia and Herzegovina) in 1943. It is painted in the three-tone camouflage of Saharian Khaki, red-brown, and gray-green applied to many late-war Italian armored vehicles.

Two M 11-39s advance across the Western Desert towards Sidi Barrani, Egypt in September of 1940. Italian forces under *Maresciallo d'Italia* (Marshal) Rodolfo Graziani reached this Egyptian port city on 16 September. High temperatures in the desert compelled the commander/turret gunner and the hull gunner to sit atop their vehicle. The driver inside the tank opened his armored vision flap to let in more air and see more of the road ahead of him. A 2 L (0.5 gallon) water bottle hangs from the commander's hatch clamp.

A 1st Battalion M 11-39 drives through the Western Desert in September of 1940. Both turret-mounted 8MM Breda Model 38 machine guns are slewed to the right. The rectangular company marking painted on the hatch has two white vertical stripes indicating the 2nd Platoon of a tank company. The numeral 2 above this marking designated the Platoon's second tank.

Fiat-Ansaldo *Carro Armato* M 11-39 Medium Tank

Length:...................4.9 M (16 feet 0.9 inches)
Width:....................2.3 M (7 feet 6.6 inches)
Height:....................2.3 M (7 feet 6.6 inches)
Combat Weight:....11,000 KG (24,250 pounds)
Armor Thickness:.6MM to 30MM
Powerplant:...........One 125 HP Fiat SPA 8T eight-cylinder, liquid-cooled, inline engine
Armament:............One 37MM Vickers-Terni L/40 gun with 84 rounds in the hull, and two 8MM Breda Model 38 Machine guns with 2808 rounds in the turret
Maximum Speed:..32 KMH (20 MPH)
Maximum Range:...210 KM (130 miles)
Crew:.....................Three

37MM Vickers-Terni L/40 Gun

Barrel Length:.........40 calibers; 1480MM (58.3 inches)
Muzzle Velocity:......640 M (3000 feet) per second
Effective Range:......7000 M (7655 yards)
Armor Penetration:.34MM at 910 M (995 yards)
Rounds:...................High Explosive (HE) and Armor-Piercing (AP)

An M 11-39 (R°E™ 2726) of the 1st Tank Battalion advances in the Western Desert during the 1940 Italian offensive, which originated in Libya. A band in (from top) red, white, and green was painted on the turret's rear to reduce the risk of friendly fire. Italian armor crews mounted captured British 23 L (6.1 gallon) fuel tanks on the engine decks of some M 11-39s, including this vehicle. The additional fuel extended the tank's endurance beyond the normal 210 KM (130 mile) range. Spare road wheels flank this fuel tank.

A VII (7th) Battalion M 13-40 tank parades through Tripoli, Libya during the arrival of the *Deutsches Afrika Korps* (DAK) on 14 February 1941. The M 13-41 was Italy's main tank during the North African campaign. It is difficult telling an M 13-40 apart from an M 14-41, because the main differences were in the power plant and other internal features. These gray-green and sand camouflaged M 13-40s have the original long fenders.

M 13-40 and M 14-41 Medium Tanks

The M 13-40 was a follow-on development of the M 11-39 and featured a revised layout. Its main armament was increased from 37MM to 47MM and was installed in a fully revolving armored turret. The twin 8MM machine guns were relocated to the fighting compartment front plate. Design work began in late 1937 and the prototype was delivered to the *Regio Esercito* in October of 1939.

The lower hull and suspension was generally similar to the earlier M 11-39. The M 13-40 also used the same 125 HP SPA 8T diesel engine. The new tank also kept the earlier vehicle's internal arrangement. Hull construction of bolted and riveted armor plate was also retained; however, the fighting compartment superstructure was enlarged to support the larger turret. The armor thickness was also increased from the M 11-39's 6MM to 30MM range to a range of 14MM to 45MM on the M 13-40.

In July of 1940, the M 13-40 entered production and was hastily pressed into service. The first battalion was sent to North Africa lacking any training for operations in this theater. The additional weight of the enlarged superstructure, new turret, and armament in a tank with the same powerplant had a detrimental effect on its performance. Almost a year was necessary to eliminate most of the M 13-40's drawbacks, but in the meantime, the British were already training with the first 27-ton American M3 Grant tanks armed with a hull-mounted 75MM gun and a turret-mounted 37MM gun. This compelled M 13-40 crews to augment their front armor with sandbags and spare track links, which increased the vehicle's weight and further decreased performance

Another early problem was the shortage of radio equipment. Extensive testing of both Italian and German radio systems had been conducted in 1940. The *Regio Esercito* selected Marelli systems – the RF 1 CA at battalion level and the RF 2 CA up to the regimental level. Production was slow to start and not all M 11-39s and early production M 13-40s were equipped. Only three vehicles of the III (3rd) Battalion were equipped with radios – one for the battalion commander and the two for company commanders mounting either a RF 1 CAT or a German-made Telefunken set. Few radios were allocated to the V (5th) battalion, while none were available for the IV (4th) and VI (6th) battalions. After the DAK (*Deutsches Afrika Korps*) arrived in Libya in early 1941, every M 13-40 eventually received the standard Marelli RF 1 CA radio equipment and M 13-40 CR (*Centro Radio*) command vehicles received an additional RF 2 CA set.

A desire to improve the M 13-40's field mobility resulted in the M 14-41. The 125 HP SPA 8T engine was replaced with a 145 HP SPA 15T powerplant. New oil filters and improved transmission gears were also added. Over 750 M 14-41s were completed and several other improvements were made during the production run. The original full-length fenders were replaced with shorter fenders after the 50th production vehicle. The engine deck cooling grills were altered to a transverse arrangement after the 492nd vehicle. Mud scrapers were fitted to the drive sprocket and the two spare roadwheels were reduced to one after the 500th M 14-41. One delay was the provision of the Putin desert compass for use in North Africa. The first compass was not mounted until December of 1942, but this was not fielded in time for service.

Delays resulted in M 14-41s not arriving in North Africa until shortly before the Battle of El Alamein in the Fall of 1942. By then, the Italian armored forces were facing ever-increasing numbers of Allied Shermans and Churchills.

This M 13-40 has difficulty crossing a ditch during training in Italy in mid-1941. M 13-40s had similar cross-county performance to the earlier M 11-39 tank. Each side of the suspension consisted of two assemblies for four double-wheeled bogies. Semi-elliptic springs carry each bogie assembly. Three return rollers support each upper track run.

German forces operated this commandeered *Lince* armored car (02+8) in Northern Italy late in World War Two. This *Lince* was equipped with additional radio equipment for use in a command role.

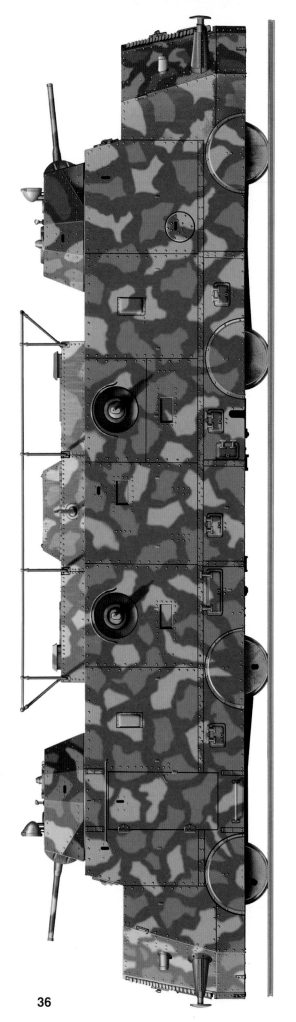

This was the first LIBLI (*Littorina Blindata*; Armored Rail Car) built for the *Regio Esercito*. LIBLI 1 was assigned to the *Genio Ferrovieri* (Railroad Engineer Corps) Regiment at Turin, Italy in September of 1942. The eight LIBLI built were primarily employed on anti-partisan operations in the Balkans.

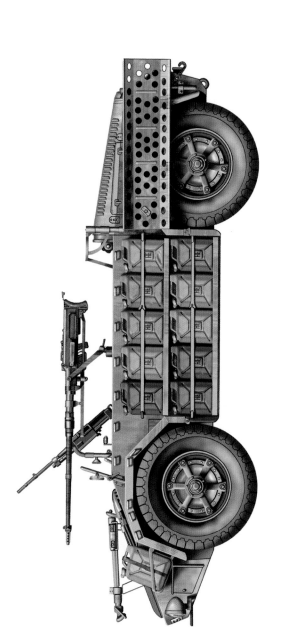

A 20mm Solothurn cannon is mounted on this *Camionetta 42* desert reconnaissance vehicle, along with an 8mm Breda Model 38 machine gun. The Saharian Group operated this vehicle from Hon, North Africa in November of 1942. Racks on the *Camionetta's* sides held 20 L (5.3 gallon) fuel and water cans.

An M 11-39 medium tank is captured in this rare color photograph during its 1938 *Regio Esercito* acceptance trials. It passed these trials and entered service in 1939. This vehicle is painted overall dark sand, with gray-green and red brown vertical streaks. The M 11-39 was armed with one 37MM gun in the right front hull and two 8MM machine guns in the turret.

(Right) This beautifully restored L 3-38 (L 35 *modificato*; modified) tankette rests on a gravel road in the Italian countryside. Red-brown patches are painted over the gray-green finish. Ansaldo modified 200 L 3s with an improved suspension, a driver's episcope, and two 8MM Breda Model 38 machine guns in mid-1942.

(Below) This table of tank markings is derived from an official *Regio Esercito* document issued in June of 1940. These tactical signs were painted on the hull or turret sides and the rear hull of Italian tanks. Battalion commanders' vehicles had the Battalion's Roman numeral in white above the sign, while individual tanks within a platoon had their number in Arabic numerals above the sign. Red designated the 1st Company, light blue the 2nd, and yellow the 3rd. Company commanders had plain rectangles, while white bars designated the three platoons in each company. Other sign colors used (not shown) were green for the 4th company, black for the Battalion Headquarters Company, and white (with black bars) for the Regimental Headquarters Company.

Commander, III (3rd) Battalion (3 Companies)

Commander, I (1st) Battalion (2 Companies)

Commander, 1st Company (Co.)

Commander, 2nd Company (Co.)

Commander, 3rd Company (Co.)

4th Tank, 1st Platoon, 1st Co.

3rd Tank, 1st Platoon, 2nd Co.

2nd Tank, 1st Platoon, 3rd Co.

M 13-40s assigned to the 1st Platoon, 1st Company, VII (7th) Battalion are unloaded at Tripoli, Libya in February of 1941. These vehicles had just been deployed from Italy and retained the overall gray-green camouflage scheme. The near vehicle is marked to represent the 1st tank of the 1st Platoon. The crewman standing on the lead tank and his two colleagues by the left side wear the dark blue overalls worn by Italian tank crewmen.

3rd Tank, 2nd Platoon, 1st Co.

4th Tank, 2nd Platoon, 2nd Co.

1st Tank, 2nd Platoon, 3rd Co.

2nd Tank, 3rd Platoon, 1st Co.

1st Tank, 3rd Platoon, 2nd Co.

4th Tank, 3rd Platoon, 3rd Co.

This was the first M 13-40 that reached the harbor at Tobruk, Libya on 20 June 1942. German and Italian forces under *Generaloberst* (Colonel General) Erwin Rommel captured Tobruk after British forces there surrendered the next day. This vehicle is the 3rd tank of the 1st Platoon, 1st Company, IX (9th) Battalion, *Ariete* Armored Division. The tank's commander stands in his turret, with both upper turret hatches opened.

The Royal Italian Army was well aware of the M 13-40's and M 14-41's deficiencies against Allied armor. The M 13 chassis was used to form the basis of the *Semovente da 75/18* assault guns. This vehicle was developed to provide the field forces with both an anti-tank and an armored artillery vehicle and as an interim step before the development of the heavy P-series tanks. The role of armored artillery was quickly found to be unsuitable and the vehicles were used simply to support the under-gunned M 13-40s. The *Semovente da 75/18* featured a revised superstructure mounting a limited traverse 75MM Ansaldo L/18 howitzer firing both high explosive and armor-piercing rounds. The vehicle carried a crew of three men.

The first *semovente* units were deployed to Libya on 18 January 1942, while two other groups remained in Italy training with the *Centauro* Armored Division. The *Carro Commando* (Command Tank) vehicles for these units were simple turretless M 13-40 (later M 14-41 or M 15-42) chassis. These command vehicles originally retained the twin 8MM machine guns, but these were replaced by a 13.2MM Breda Model 31 heavy machine gun in 1942. Each vehicle was fitted with Marelli RF 1 CA and RF 2 CA radios and a rangefinder.

Experience in North Africa resulted in one company per tank battalion being equipped with M 14-41s and the other two companies receiving *semoventi* (self-propelled guns) during the Fall of 1942. Mussolini ordered this unit reorganization in July of that year, instead of a *Regio Esercito* proposal for two tank companies and one assault company in each tank battalion.

During the Spring of 1942, a proposal was made to strengthen the divisional artillery regiment by equipping them with the powerful new *Semovente da 90/53*, a tank destroyer/self-propelled gun designed and built by Ansaldo. The *Semovente da 90/53* mounted a 90MM Ansaldo *Cannone da 90/53* dual-purpose (anti-aircraft/anti-tank) gun on a modified M 14-41 chassis. The 90/53 gun was similar to the famous German 88MM *Flak* 36/37; however, the Italian weapon had a slightly higher muzzle velocity (840 M/2756 feet per second, versus 820 M/2690 feet per second for the *Flak 36/37*). The 90/53 could defeat any tank armor of its time. The vehicle's interior and superstructure were re-arranged to accommodate two crewmen in front, a centrally mounted engine, and the open gun mount and two additional crewmen at the rear. The gun was shielded at the front, top, and sides, but open to rear. Only eight rounds were carried internally, which required a modified L 6-40 ammunition carrier with 24 rounds towing a trailer with 40 more rounds. The *Semovente da 90/53* suffered from reduced mobility due to its increased weight while powered by the same 145 HP SPA engine used in the M 14-41 tank.

The three units equipped with *Semoventi da 90/53* were initially kept in reserve in Northern Italy. The Army Supreme Command was uncertain whether they should go to Egypt or to Russia where the Italian 8th Army was waiting for a weapon able to counter the Soviet T-34 tank. *Semoventi da 90/53* were deployed to Sicily in response to the Allied landings on 10 July 1943, where they faced heavier British and American armored vehicles.

An M 13-40 (RₒEₜₒ 3123) assigned to the IX (9th) Battalion, *Ariete* Armored Division is loaded onto a Viberti tank recovery trailer. A Lancia 3/Ro truck hauled this two axle trailer. The Roman numeral IX that designated the Battalion were painted on both the tank and the trailer. The trailer's white number plate displays the registration RₒEₜₒ 8489R. RₒEₜₒ (the abbreviation for *Regio Esercito*) and R (*Rimorchio*; Trailer) were red, while the numerals were black. A shortage of tank transport trailers required many M 13-40s to advance to front-line positions under their own power. This increased wear and tear on the tanks' tracks and suspensions.

A late production M 14-41 (R̥oEᴛᴏ 4886) is parked near El Alamein, Egypt in mid-1942. Axis forces reached the outskirts of this town – only 97 ᴋᴍ (60 miles) from the key port city of Alexandria – in July. This marked the easternmost advance by the Axis in North Africa during World War Two. The M 14-41 had a 145 ʜᴘ Fiat SPA 15T engine that generated 20 ʜᴘ more than the unit that powered the similar M 13-40. An 8ᴍᴍ Breda Model 38 machine gun was mounted on the roof of this tank's turret. It provided some protection against Allied aircraft and had an Anti-Aircraft (AA) sight mounted atop its barrel.

This M 14-41 in North Africa was assigned to the XIII (13th) Battalion, whose tactical markings were painted on the turret sides. The vehicle is also equipped with an 8ᴍᴍ AA machine gun on the turret roof. Early M 14-41s were equipped with short fenders.

47ᴍᴍ Ansaldo 47/32 Gun

Barrel Length:	32.4 calibers; 1525ᴍᴍ (60 inches)
Muzzle Velocity:	630 ᴍ (2067 feet) per second
Rate of Fire:	20-35 rounds per minute
Maximum Range:	6000 ᴍ (6562 yards)
Armor Penetration:	50ᴍᴍ at 400 ᴍ (437 yards)
Rounds:	High Explosive (HE) and Armor-Piercing (AP)

Four M 14-41 medium tanks advance under enemy fire at el-Guettar, Tunisia in late March of 1943. These tanks were among 16 M 14-41s assigned to the 131st *Centauro* Armored Division that attacked US forces advancing on Tunis. The tanks and two *Semoventi da 75* of the Division's XIV (14) Battalion were supported in their assault by four *Autonannoni da 90/53* of the DII (502nd) Group. El-Guettar was one of *Centauro*'s last battles prior to the surrender of Axis forces in North Africa on 9 May 1943.

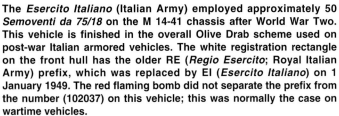

The *Esercito Italiano* (Italian Army) employed approximately 50 *Semoventi da 75/18* on the M 14-41 chassis after World War Two. This vehicle is finished in the overall Olive Drab scheme used on post-war Italian armored vehicles. The white registration rectangle on the front hull has the older RE (*Regio Esercito*; Royal Italian Army) prefix, which was replaced by EI (*Esercito Italiano*) on 1 January 1949. The red flaming bomb did not separate the prefix from the number (102037) on this vehicle; this was normally the case on wartime vehicles.

Support straps for three 20 L (5.3 gallon) fuel cans ('jerrycans') are mounted on the left superstructure of the same *Semovente da 75/18*. Each *semovente* carried up to eight 20 L cans, which extended the vehicle's 200 KM (124 mile) range. Fairings on the superstructure roof protected both antennas for the Canadian No 19 radio fitted to post-war *semoventi*.

This AB 43 armored car was restored to its wartime condition in 2001. The *Autoblinda* (Armored Car) AB 43 was the final development of the AB 40-41 series, which saw extensive service in North Africa. The AB 43 was armed with one 20MM cannon in the turret. It was standardized for production at the time of the Italian Armistice in 1943 and was built until the Second World War ended in 1945.

This new M tank – either an M 13-40 or M 14-41 – is parked in Italy awaiting shipment to Libya. The vehicle has the short fenders common on late production M 13-40s and early production M 14-41s. Lack of tactical markings is due to this tank being an attrition replacement for a frontline unit. Two of the 8MM Breda Model 38 machine guns were mounted in the right forward hull. Brake inspection hatches are opened on the forward hull between the drive sprockets.

Fiat-Ansaldo *Carro Armato* M 13-40 Medium Tank

Length:....................4.9 M (16 feet 1 inch)
Width:....................2.3 M (7 feet 6.6 inches)
Height:....................2.4 M (7 feet 10.5 inches)
Combat Weight:.....14,000 KG (30,864 pounds)
Armor Thickness:..14MM to 45MM
Powerplant:.............One 125 HP Fiat SPA 8T eight-cylinder, liquid-cooled, inline engine.
Armament:.............One 47MM Ansaldo 47/32 gun with 104 rounds and one 8MM Breda Model 38 machine gun with 120 rounds in turret; provision for one 8MM Breda Model 38 machine gun with 120 rounds on turret root; and two 8MM Breda Model 38 machine guns with 2808 rounds in right front hull.
Maximum Speed:...30 KMH (19 MPH)
Maximum Range:...200 KM (124 miles)
Crew:.......................Four

Fiat-Ansaldo *Carro Armato* M 14-41 Medium Tank

Same as for M 13-14, except:
Combat Weight:.....14,500 KG (31,966 pounds)
Powerplant:.............One 145 HP Fiat SPA 15T eight-cylinder, liquid-cooled, inline engine
Armament:.............One 47MM Ansaldo 47/32 gun with 87 rounds in the turret; two 8MM Breda Model 38 machine guns with 2664 rounds in the hull.
Maximum Speed:...32 KMH (20 MPH)

The Commander stands in the turret of his M 14-41 *Centro Radio* command vehicle. This variant was equipped with two radio antennas – one forward, one aft – along the right upper hull. The aft antenna worked with additional radio equipment located on this variant. The M 14-41 was armed with the effective 47MM 47/32 tank gun. One 8MM Breda Model 38 machine gun was mounted coaxial with the main gun. Two additional 8MM weapons were placed in a gimbal mount on the right superstructure.

This M 14-41 is parked at Bellinzago, near Milan, Italy during the 1950s. A longer 47MM 47/40 gun replaced this vehicle's turret-mounted 47MM 47/32. A 13.2MM Breda Model 31 machine gun replaced the two hull-mounted 8MM Breda Model 38 machine guns. These weapons were only for experimental purpose and were not adopted on standard M 14-41s. One Model 38 gun peers out of the turret. An L 3-35 tankette is parked beside the tank.

Like other armies, the *Regio Esercito* attempted to recover disabled tanks from the battlefield for repair at rear area depots. An SPA TM 40 artillery tractor is connected to a trailer, which is unloading an M 15-42 tank. This tank was a development of the M 13-40 and M 14-41 with a longer 47MM gun and a 190 HP engine.

An early production M 13-40 moves through wooded terrain during training. Early production vehicles had long smooth fenders, which were reduced in size on later production tanks. This M 13-40 also has the simple radiator cover on the aft engine deck; later vehicles had the radiator cap moved aft atop this cover and an overhang placed on the cover's right and left edges. Two spare road wheels mounted at the rear of the engine deck facilitated field repairs.

A crewman examines the engine deck of a 3rd production series M 13-40 in North Africa in either 1941 or 1942. A 3rd Platoon insignia is painted on the hull side above the Roman battalion numeral VII (7). The M 13-40 received gray-green mottling over its Saharian Khaki finish. A white cross painted on the turret roof was an aircraft recognition marking. (Bundesarchiv)

Sandbags for additional protection are placed on the forward hull of this M 13-40 in North Africa in 1942. Markings on the turret indicate this is the 4th vehicle of a company's 3rd Platoon. The commander stands in his turret opening, with an 8mm Breda Model 38 mounted for AA use beside this opening. Another crewman rides atop the engine deck, while a tarpaulin is draped over some items on this deck. (Bundesarchiv)

Tank and Armored Car Markings

All vehicles were given a simple and effective system of markings. The markings were common to all detachments and allowed the instant identification of any vehicle from any formation, ranging from platoon to regiment.

The battalion (group) markings were painted on the sides and on the right rear hull. A rectangle was segmented with the company colors – red for the 1st Company, light blue for the 2nd, yellow for the 3rd, and green for the 4th. The regiment number was painted in white Arabic numbers on the left edge of the rear superstructure. The battalion numbers, either on the opposite edge or at the right rear hull, used 10 CM (3.9 inches) high Roman numerals. For units up to the VII (7th) M tank battalion, it was painted under the rectangle.

The company commander's vehicle had a solid rectangle, while platoon vehicles had one (1st Platoon), two (2nd), or three (3rd) white vertical bars on the rectangle. The tank number in the platoon was painted in the same color as its company over the rectangle. Vehicles assigned to the battalion headquarters company had black rectangles, while the regimental headquarters company used white rectangles with black vertical bars.

On turreted vehicles, the markings appeared on the front sides and turret rear. Although the marking positions were approved and ordered into use in October of 1940, they were not in common use until late 1941.

A divisional insignia was also used, although this was not considered an official marking. The 131st *Centauro* Armored Division (AD) used a black centaur, the 132nd *Ariete* AD employed a ram's head, and the 133rd *Littorio* AD sometimes used a bundle of fasces under the horsemen on a tank.

The air recognition marking initially consisted of a white cross and later a 70 CM (27.6 inch) diameter white disk painted on the front of the M tank turret roof or the engine covers of tankettes. The regimental badge and the national colors of green, white, and red were occasionally painted on tanks.

Two *Ariete* Armored Division M 13-40s are parked near each other in North Africa during 1941-42. The near tank is assigned to the 1st Platoon, VII (7th) Battalion, while the far vehicle belonged to the 3rd Platoon of the same Battalion. Both commanders wear the black leather crew helmets and dark blue overalls. (Bundesarchiv)

A British shell destroyed this *Littorio* Armored Division M 14-41 *Centro Radio* (RₒEₜₒ 3493) during the Battle of El Alamein in November of 1942. This vehicle has the late radiator cover with overhang along the left and right edges. Detonation of the fuel and ammunition blew the turret off the vehicle and scattered five fuel cans towards the tank's rear. This command tank was assigned to the Division's head-quarters during the battle.

The *Semovente da 75/18* assault gun was an M 13-40 or M 14-41 chassis modified with a 75ᴍᴍ Ansaldo L/18 howitzer. This weapon entered *Regio Esercito* service as a field artillery piece in 1935. The L/18 was fitted to the front of an enclosed superstructure on the *Semovente*'s hull. Fiat and Ansaldo developed the first prototype using a modified M 13-40, which was completed in early 1941. The *Regio Esercito* deployed the first *semoventi* (plural of *semovente*) to North Africa in January of 1942.

(Below Left) The *Semovente da 75/18* prototype based on the M 14-41 is parked outside Ansaldo's Genoa factory in 1942. A rectangular armored flap for the driver's vision slot was located to left of the 75ᴍᴍ howitzer.

Fiat-Ansaldo *Semovente da 75/18* Assault Gun (on M 13-40 chassis)

Length:....................4.9 ᴍ (16 feet 1 inch)
Width:.....................2.3 ᴍ (7 feet 6.6 inches
Height:....................1.9 ᴍ (6 feet 2.8 inches)
Combat Weight:......13,100 ᴋɢ (28,880 pounds)
Armor Thickness:..6ᴍᴍ to 30ᴍᴍ
Powerplant:............One 125 ʜᴘ Fiat SPA 8V eight-cylinder, liquid-cooled, inline engine
Armament:.............One 75ᴍᴍ Ansaldo L/18 gun with 44 rounds in the hull; one 8ᴍᴍ Breda Model 38 machine gun with 1104 rounds on the roof. (Early vehicles had one 6.5ᴍᴍ Breda Model 30 machine gun on the roof.)
Maximum Speed:...31 ᴋᴍʜ (19 ᴍᴘʜ)
Maximum Range:...200 ᴋᴍ (124 miles)
Crew:......................Three

Fiat-Ansaldo *Semovente da 75/32* Assault Gun (on M 14-41 chassis)

Same as for *Semovente da 75/18*, except:
Combat Weight:.....14,000 ᴋɢ (30,864 pounds)
Armament:.............One 75ᴍᴍ Ansaldo L/32 gun with 44 rounds in hull.

Italian *semoventi* on M tank chassis were originally armed with the 75ᴍᴍ L/18 howitzer, which was fitted with a 'pepperbox' muzzle brake. This device reduced the gun's recoil when fired. The L/18 was effective up to 8000 ᴍ (8749 yards) in direct fire. *Semovente* crews manually elevated this weapon +22˚ to -12˚, and slewed it from 20˚ left to 18˚ right. The Italians employed *Semoventi da 75/18* in service up to the mid-1950s.

The *Semovente da 75/18*'s fighting compartment accommodated three crewman. The driver sat to the left of the 75mm gun, while the commander/gunner was situated to the right and the loader behind and to right of the gun. Each *Semovente da 75/18* carried 44 rounds of High Explosive (HE), Armor-Piercing (AP), and High Explosive Squash Head (HESH) ammunition.

75mm Ansaldo L/18 Gun

Barrel Length:..........18 calibers; 1350mm (53.1 inches)
Muzzle Velocity:.......430 m (1411 feet) per second
Effective Range:......8000 m (8749 yards)
Rate of Fire:............10 rounds per minute
Armor Penetration:.59mm
Rounds:...................High Explosive (HE), Armor-Piercing (AP), and High-Explosive Squash Head (HESH)

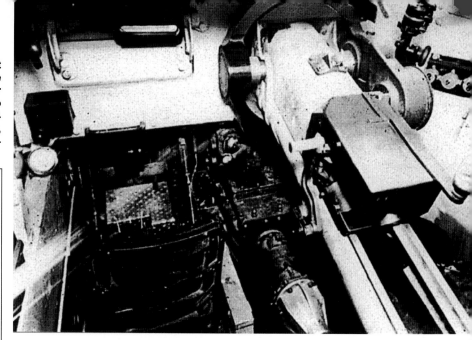

An early *Carro Commando per Semovente* command vehicle rolls through North Africa in 1942. This variant was based on the M 13-40 and was armed with two 8mm Breda Model 38 machine guns, instead of the *Semovente da 75/18*'s hull-mounted 75mm howitzer. A crew of four – commander, driver, and two machine gunners – manned each vehicle. Four *Carro Commando* vehicles were assigned to each *semovente* battalion.

Fiat-Ansaldo *Carro Comando per Semovente* Command Vehicle (on M 14-41 chassis)

Length:.................4.9 m (16 feet 1 inch)
Width:...................2.3 m (7 feet 6.6 inches)
Height:.................1.9 m (6 feet 2.8 inches)
Combat Weight:...12,500 kg (27,557 pounds)
Powerplant:..........One 145 hp Fiat SPA 15T eight-cylinder, liquid-cooled, inline engine
Armament:...........One 13.2mm Breda Model 31 machine gun with 404 rounds in the hull; one 8mm Breda Model 38 machine gun with 504 rounds on the roof.
Maximum Speed:.32 kmh (20 mph)
Maximum Range:.200 km (124 miles)
Crew:...................Four

Ansaldo developed a later *Carro Commando per Semovente* on the M 14-41 chassis in 1942. This vehicle replaced the two hull-mounted 8mm machine guns with one 13.2mm Breda Model 31 machine gun. Four outward-opening hatches on the fighting compartment roof provided easy crew access. An 8mm Breda Model 38 for anti-aircraft use was mounted inside the fighting compartment.

Ansaldo experimentally fitted a 75MM Ansaldo 75/32 Model 37 field gun into an M 41 *semovente*. This weapon's longer barrel provided a greater range and muzzle velocity than the L/18 gun; however, the *Regio Esercito* preferred the L/34 gun for later *semoventi*. The 75/32-armed *semovente* was cancelled in 1942.

This *aero cooperazione* (air cooperation) variant of the *Carro Commando per Semovente M 15-42* was built in small numbers. It replaced one of two RF 2 CA radios fitted to most *Carro Commando* vehicles with an RF 3 M2 ground-to-air radio. A Forward Air Controller (FAC) in the vehicle communicated with Italian aircraft operating in support of ground forces. It retained the 13.2MM hull-mounted machine gun. All *Carro Commando* vehicles had two whip-type radio antennas mounted on the forward superstructure.

75MM Ansaldo L/34 Gun

Barrel Length:........34 calibers; 2550MM (100.4 inches)
Muzzle Velocity:.....525 M (1722 feet) per second
Effective Range:....8700 M (9514 yards)
Rounds:..................High Explosive (HE) and Armor-Piercing (AP)

A *Semovente da 75/34* assigned to the *Ariete* Armored Division is parked in Rome in September of 1943. The 75MM Ansaldo L/34 gun had a 34-caliber (2550MM/100.4 inch) long barrel, compared to the Ansaldo L/18's 18-caliber (1350MM/53.1 inch) long barrel. The newer weapon had a muzzle velocity of 525 M (1722 feet) per second and an effective range of 8700M (9514 yards). These figures were superior to the L/18's 430 M (1411 feet) per second muzzle velocity and 8000 M (8749 yard) range. The *Semovente da 75/34* entered *Regio Esercito* service in the summer of 1943 and was issued to two tank destroyer battalions.

Italy's most powerful tank destroyer was the *Semovente da 90/53*, which Ansaldo developed in 1942. A 90MM Ansaldo *Canone da 90/53* anti-aircraft gun was mounted on a lengthened and modified M 14-41 hull. The *Canone da 90/53* anti-aircraft gun was first produced in late 1939 and entered *Regio Esercito* service early the next year. This weapon had a muzzle velocity of 840 M (2756 feet) per second and an effective range of 12,000 M (13,123 yards). Its Armor-Piercing (AP) rounds could penetrate 206MM of armor. The *Regio Escercito* ordered just 30 *Semoventi da 90/53* before the Italian Armistice in September of 1943.

The 90MM *Canone da 90/53* was mounted on the *semovente*'s aft hull, with the 125 HP Fiat SPA 15T engine moved from the aft hull to the mid-hull area. An armored shield was mounted around the gun's breech area for crew protection. The gun barrel rested inside a travel lock mounted on the upper front hull. This lock stabilized the gun during extended travel to and from the front.

Fiat-Ansaldo *Semovente da 90/53* M41 Self-Propelled Anti-Tank Gun (on M 14-41 chassis)

Length:	5.2 M (17 feet 0.7 inches)
Width:	2.3 M (7 feet 6.6 inches)
Height:	2.3 M (7 feet 6.6 inches)
Combat Weight:	17,000 KG (37,478 pounds)
Armor Thickness:	6MM to 30MM
Powerplant:	One 125 HP Fiat SPA 15T eight-cylinder, liquid-cooled, inline engine
Armament:	One 90MM *Canone de 90/53* gun with six rounds in the rear hull
Maximum Speed:	25 KMH (16 MPH)
Maximum Range:	150 KM (93 miles)
Crew:	Four

The *Semovente da 90/53*'s gun shield was mounted over the 90MM gun's breech section. This vehicle retained the two brake inspection hatches mounted on the lower front hull. Long fenders were mounted above the tracks to reduce the amount of dust, sand, and rocks flung up onto the hull.

The *Semovente da 90/53*'s 90MM gun had an elevation range of -5° to +24°, while it could be traversed up to 40° left and right. This vehicle was 5.2 M (17 feet 0.7 inches) long, a 0.3 M (11.8 inch) increase over the M 14-41's 4.9 M (16 foot 1 inch) length. Both vehicles had the same basic suspension, which featured four double-wheeled articulated bogies.

The gun shield provided some protection from front and overhead projectiles and shrapnel for the *Semovente da 90/53*'s crew. Two vision slots are cut into the shield's roof. Radio equipment was installed to the left of the gun's breech, while crew seats flank the gun. The four-man crew consisted of a commander, gunner, loader, and driver.

Semovente Markings

Initially, *Semoventi da 75/18* were issued to artillery battalions consisting of two batteries of four gun vehicles. Each battery originally consisted of four (later five) gun vehicles, one command vehicle and, according to the Table of Organization and Equipment (TOE), a single L 3-35 tankette.

The battalion/group consisted of two (later three) batteries, a headquarters component, two command vehicles, and a reserve element of one command vehicle and two or three gun vehicles.

The M tank battalion organization was later revised to include a single M tank company and two *semovente* companies. The *semoventi* wore their own particular insignia from January to October of 1942 – a yellow downward-pointed triangle with black top and trim – but wore the standard tank tactical markings once they were incorporated into the tank battalions.

90MM Ansaldo *Canone de 90/53* Gun

Barrel Length:........53 calibers; 4770MM (187.8 inches)
Muzzle Velocity:......710 M (2329 feet) per second
Effective Range:......14,500 M (15,857 yards)
Rounds:...................Armor-Piercing (AP)
Armor Penetration:.206MM

A *Semovente da 90/53* (left) and its L 6-40 *trasporto munizioni* (ammunition carrier) conduct exercises on the Nettunia firing range near Rome in the Summer of 1942. The *semovente* carried just six ready rounds in the rear hull, which required the services of the ammunition carrier for sustained fire. Each 90MM projectile weighed 10.3 KG (22.7 pounds).

An L 6-40 *trasporto munizioni* (RᵒEᵀᵒ 5562) hitched to an ammunition trailer is parked on a city street. This modification of the L 6-40 light tank carried 90ᴍᴍ ammunition in side-mounted bins. The trailer carried additional ammunition for the *Semovente da 90/53*. This ammunition carrier did not carry any armament.

The single-axle ammunition trailer was hooked up to the L 6-40 *trasporto munizioni* via a single pintel. This pintel was connected to a towing eye on the L 6-40's rear hull. Both ammunition bin hatches on the *trasporto munizioni* opened forward, while the two roof-mounted crew access hatches opened aft.

German troops captured this *Semovente da 90/53* on its flatcar at a Rome railroad station. This occurred after an Allied air raid in March of 1944. The Germans painted a *Balkenkreuz* (Beam Cross) national insignia over the original Italian unit marking on the gun shield side.

The M 15-42 was the final M tank developed during World War Two. It was armed with a turret-mounted 47MM Ansaldo L/40 gun and two hull-mounted 8MM machine guns. The M 15-42 was just entering *Regio Esercito* service at the time of the Armistice of 8 September 1943. German forces seized the few M 15-42s built after that date and employed them in northern Italy and the Balkans.

M 15-42 Medium Tank

The Italians studied an improved M 14-41 variant as a stopgap vehicle in anticipation of the heavier P 40. This vehicle was designated the M 15-42 and featured a slightly longer hull and chassis equipped with a 190 HP SPA 15 TB gasoline engine. The more powerful engine provided a speed of 40 KMH (25 MPH) in comparison to the 30-32 KMH (19 to 20 MPH) speed of the earlier M 13-40s and M 14-41s. The M 15-42 was also equipped with an improved 47MM Ansaldo 47/40 gun. The longer barrel provided increased muzzle velocity, which translated into a flatter trajectory, increased range, and greater striking power. The superstructure featured a revised engine deck, and slightly thicker armor, while the hull crew access door was moved from the left side to the right side. M 15-42 CR (*Centro Radio*; Radio Center) command vehicles deleted the two hull mounted 8MM machine guns and added radios and a second antenna. M 15-42s sent to North Africa – like late production M 14-41s – were fitted with additional 20 L 'jerrycan' supports on the left superstructure and front hull. Late production M 15-42s replaced the second spare road wheel with rear mounted smoke generators.

A self-propelled anti-aircraft variant mounting a quad 20MM Scotti cannon was designed and tested in 1943, but appeared too late for mass production before the 3 September Armistice. Few M 15-42 (also called M 42) tanks were produced during 1942-43, as the Army Staff preferred using these hulls for assault guns armed with either the 75MM L/18 gun or the more powerful 75MM L/34 weapon.

In the meantime, the armored artillery had a continuing requirement for larger caliber self-propelled guns. A new *Semovente* design using an enlarged M 42 chassis was studied in early 1943. This vehicle was designated the M 43 and represented the largest and heaviest of the M tanks developed during the war. It had a 105MM 105/25 gun and increased armor protection. The *Semovente da 105/25* M 43 – nicknamed *Bassotto* (Dachshund) – had the potential of being the best Italian armored vehicle of World War Two, but few were delivered before the Armistice. Some M 43s were equipped with the 75MM L/34 guns already mounted on the M 42.

Fiat-Ansaldo *Carro Armato* M 15-42 Medium Tank

Length:...................5 M (16 feet 4.8 inches)
Width:....................2.2 M (7 feet 2.6 inches)
Height:...................2.4 M (7 feet 10.5 inches)
Combat Weight:....15,000 KG (33,069 pounds)
Armor Thickness:.6MM to 42MM
Powerplant:...........One 190 HP Fiat SPA 15 TB eight-cylinder, liquid-cooled, inline engine
Armament:.............One 47MM Ansaldo L/40 gun with 111 rounds in turret; one 8MM Breda Model 38 machine gun with 120 rounds co-axial with main gun; and two 8MM Breda Model 38 machine guns with 2520 rounds in right front hull.
Maximum Speed:..40 KMH (25 MPH)
Maximum Range:..220 KM (137 miles)
Crew:......................Four

47MM Ansaldo L/40 Gun

Length of Gun Barrel:.40 calibers; 1880MM (74 inches)
Muzzle Velocity:...........829 M (2720 feet) per second
Effective Range:..........7000 M (7655 yards)
Rounds:........................High Explosive (HE) and Armor-Piercing (AP)
Armor Penetration:......42MM at 1000 M (1094 yards)

The crew of this *Ariete II* Armored Division M 15-42 (REᴵᵒ 5052) added tree branches for additional camouflage. This vehicle rolls at high speed during exercises in northwest Italy in May of 1943. The 190 HP Fiat SPA 15 TB engine gave the M 15-42 a maximum speed of 40 KMH (25 MPH).

Three of the 11 *Semovente da 75/46* assault guns Ansaldo completed are assembled at the factory in 1944. This vehicle was an uparmored M 43 armed with a 75ᴍᴍ Ansaldo L/46 gun. Late war *semoventi* were camouflaged in a three-tone scheme of Saharian Khaki, red-brown, and gray-green.

Fiat-Ansaldo *Semovente da 75/34* M 42 Self-Propelled Anti-Tank Gun (on M 14-42 chassis)

Length:...................5 ᴍ (16 feet 4.8 inches)
Width:.....................2.3 ᴍ (7 feet 6.6 inches)
Height:...................1.8 ᴍ (5 feet 10.9 inches)
Combat Weight:....15,000 ᴋɢ (33,069 pounds)
Armor Thickness:.15ᴍᴍ to 60ᴍᴍ
Powerplant:...........One 190 ʜᴘ Fiat SPA 15 TB eight-cylinder, liquid-cooled, inline engine
Armament:.............One 75ᴍᴍ Ansaldo L/46 gun with 42 rounds and one 8ᴍᴍ Breda Model 38 machine gun with 888 rounds in hull.
Maximum Speed:..40 ᴋᴍʜ (25 ᴋᴍʜ)
Maximum Range:..220 ᴋᴍ (137 miles)
Crew:.....................Three

Fiat-Ansaldo *Semovente da 105/25* M 43 Self-Propelled Anti-Tank Gun (on M 43 chassis)

Length:...................5.1 ᴍ (16 feet 8.8 inches)
Width:.....................2.4 ᴍ (7 feet 10.5 inches)
Height:...................1.8 ᴍ (5 feet 10.9 inches)
Combat Weight:....16,000 ᴋɢ (35,273 pounds)
Armor Thickness:.14ᴍᴍ to 70ᴍᴍ
Powerplant:...........One 190 ʜᴘ Fiat SPA 15 TB eight-cylinder, liquid-cooled, inline engine
Armament:.............One 105ᴍᴍ L/25 gun with 48 rounds and one 8ᴍᴍ Breda Model 38 machine gun with 888 rounds in hull.
Maximum Speed:..35 ᴋᴍʜ (22 ᴋᴍʜ)
Maximum Range:..170 ᴋᴍ (106 miles)
Crew:.....................Three

75ᴍᴍ Ansaldo L/46 Gun

Barrel Length:..............46 calibers; 3450ᴍᴍ (135.8 inches)
Muzzle Velocity:...........750 ᴍ (2461 feet) per second
Effective Range:..........13,740 ᴍ (15,026 yards)
Rounds:.......................High Explosive (HE) and Armor-Piercing (AP)

105ᴍᴍ L/25 Gun

Barrel Length:..............25 calibers; 2625ᴍᴍ (103.3 inches)
Muzzle Velocity:...........510 ᴍ (1673 feet) per second
Effective Range:..........4544 ᴍ (4969 yards)
Armor Penetration:......100ᴍᴍ
Rounds:.......................High Explosive (HE) and Armor-Piercing (AP)

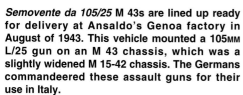

Semovente da 105/25 M 43s are lined up ready for delivery at Ansaldo's Genoa factory in August of 1943. This vehicle mounted a 105ᴍᴍ L/25 gun on an M 43 chassis, which was a slightly widened M 15-42 chassis. The Germans commandeered these assault guns for their use in Italy.

P 40 Heavy Tank

P (*Pesante*; Heavy) tanks were called for in the 1938 armored troop regulations; however, protracted development and other priorities delayed an order until July of 1940. Both the military and Ansaldo prepared several designs, and Benito Mussolini approved a 25 MT (28 ton) vehicle on 7 August 1940. Its projected armament was one 75MM Ansaldo L/34 main gun and a 20MM Breda Model 35 co-axial cannon in a rotating turret. The vehicle was also to be armed with three to four machine guns. It had a crew of five men and its 330 HP Ansaldo diesel engine would provide a speed of 40 KMH (25 MPH). The prototype, provisionally named the P 75 (after the main gun caliber), was to be ready after one year.

Design changes, the war situation, and study of the Soviet T-34 tank prolonged the new tank's development. The resulting P 40 was highly different from the original mock-up and was not ready for three years. Orders were further delayed due to the *Commando Supremo* (Army Supreme Command) favoring production of the German *Panzerkampfwagen IV* (*B.W. Serie 7*). The Germans had offered a PzKpfw IV production license for 30 million Deutschmarks in March of 1943. This proposal called for delivering the drawings and a single tank to both Fiat and Ansaldo within 112 days, while another vehicle was provided to the Italian War Ministry. The first five months of production (130 tanks per month) were to be reserved for Italy. After five months, half of the production run would be allocated for the German Army and the rest for Italy. The plan to produce and procure PzKpfw IV tanks for the *Regio Esercito* (Royal Italian Army) did not come to fruition.

The first 500 P 40 heavy tanks were ordered on 22 April 1942, but this order was increased to 579 vehicles the following October. An SPA document indicates the first production P 40 tanks were to be prepared for final inspection in August of 1943, while the first heavy tank battalion was to be activated on 8 August and the second on 1 September – two days before the Armistice. Several PzKpfw V Panther tanks were also to be purchased from Germany, while a P 43 tank armed with a 90MM gun was under development.

Ansaldo's records (9 September 1943 to 31 March 1945) indicated only one P 40 was produced and finished prior to the Armistice. Twenty-three P 40s were completed in late 1943, but 11 of them lacked engines. Seventy-seven more heavy tanks were completed in 1944, but 29 of these did not have powerplants, and none were produced in 1945. The P 40 was the only non-German tank produced for the *Wehrmacht* (German Armed Forces) during 1943-44.

The P 40 heavy tank was the best Italian armored vehicle in World War Two. The hull was divided into a driver's compartment, fighting compartment, and engine compartment and was made of special armor plate bolted to internal rigid steel plates. The lower hull armor, ranging from 14MM to 50MM in thickness, was riveted and waterproofed for wading. Angled bars strengthened the armor-plated floor.

The front mounted driver's compartment also housed the transmission. This was bolted to a small block and to the front angled armor plate, together with the linkage control frame. The transmission employed a dry disc clutch, a five-speed plus reverse gearbox, and epicyclic steering with pneumatic (air-powered) brakes. A small hatch in the front plate opened from inside the vehicle and provided additional access to the transmission and differential components.

This compartment had a large direct vision port with an armored flap sufficiently sized for crew entry. An episcope was mounted over the armored flap. An antenna mount was located on the left front corner of the upper hull, while a pistol port was mounted on the right side. No hull machine gun was fitted.

The fighting compartment and turret ring occupied the center section. Sloped superstructure front and side armor consisted of 20MM to 50MM plates riveted together. Full-length fenders were fitted over the track runs. The rear fender section was used to mount both the air intake filters and the exhaust mufflers.

A fully revolving turret mounting a 75MM L/34 gun was located above the fighting compartment. The turret armor consisted of riveted 40MM to 50MM thick plates. The turret face was further protected by a 50MM thick rounded gun mantlet. An armored air intake was mounted across the upper rear turret plate, while a stowage bin was welded across the lower rear turret plate. A large, one-piece sliding hatch occupied the rear half of the turret roof. The turret roof was also equipped with two episcopes, one each for the commander and the loader. The turret side and rear plates were also fitted with narrow vision/pistol port slits. The P 40 used the same Marelli RF 1 CA radio equipment as the M tanks.

The 75MM L/34 main gun and a co-axial 8MM Breda Model 38 machine gun – which replaced the 20MM cannon – were mounted in the turret front. The gun system consisted of the weapons, cradle, recuperators, and the traverse and elevation controls. The turret was equipped with manual and power traverse. The guns were aimed with telescopes and were fired using either a foot or hand trigger. The co-axial machine gun could be removed and used as an anti-aircraft weapon if needed. Late production P 40s had a second 8MM machine gun mounted on the turret roof. The main gun ammunition was carried in boxes on the hull floor and in saddles mounted on the inside of the hull structure. Machine gun ammunition was carried in wooden racks inside the main fighting compartment. A 9MM Beretta Model 38/43 sub-machine gun could be fired from inside the vehicle.

The engine compartment in the rear of the vehicle was supported by four side members. It contained the diesel power plant, two fans, two radiators, and the main and auxiliary fuel tanks – one on each side. A transverse frame between the engine and radiators helped to improve the vehicle's structural integrity.

Early production P 40s were powered by an electrically started, liquid cooled, 330 HP SPA 8V 12-cylinder, liquid-cooled, inline diesel engine. Hand starting was also an option using an outside handcrank. The vehicle was equipped with a heater to warm the coolant when operating in cold climates.

The engine deck consisted of five parts: a

Ansaldo completed the P 40 heavy tank prototype in early 1942. This 26 MT (28.7 ton) vehicle was armed with a 75MM L/34 gun and a co-axial 8MM Breda Model 38 machine gun in the turret. Only one production P 40 was completed before the Italian Armistice of 3 September 1943.

central grill, two radiator grills, and two engine compartment inspection doors. A winch system was mounted on the hull rear and was used for recovery and towing.

The P 40's running gear consisted of a front mounted double drive sprocket, four bogie assemblies (two per side), an adjustable rear idler, and four track return rollers to support the upper track run. Each bogie assembly utilized semi-elliptical laminated leaf springs to support four pairs of road wheels. The overall suspension design was similar to that used on the M series tanks.

A spare road wheel was mounted at the hull rear, flanked by a smoke candle rack to the left and a small toolbox to the right. A 500 W Garelli generator for the batteries and radios and a jack were located at the rear end of the left fender. Another small toolbox was mounted on the right fender's aft end. A track clamp and pioneer tools were also fastened to the fenders. Spare track shoes were carried on the engine deck.

The *Regio Esercito* issued the *Impiego delle GG. UU. Corazzate* (Employment of the Armored Major Units) in August of 1941, which superceded the 1938 regulations. This new document called for *Semoventi da 75/18* to temporarily fulfill the P 40's tactical functions until sufficient P 40s were available. The May 1943 procurement plan called for 190 P 40s to be delivered in August of 1943, 25 in September, 30 in October, 30 more in November, and 45 in December. Each P 40 battalion of three companies was to have 40 tanks, a command armored car, and two M 43 command vehicles. The remainder of the 360 vehicles on order were to be built and delivered in 1944.

The 3 September 1943 Armistice ended the P 40 program. The newly formed battalions were dissolved, and the work interrupted. According to Ansaldo, the Germans ordered 150 P 40s, but only 101 were built. A number of these were issued to three armored companies – two for the *Schutzpolizei* (Protection Police), activated in July and December of 1944, and one to *Waffen-SS Grenadier Brigade* 24, which was formed in July of 1944. Each company had 15 P 40s and they were primarily engaged in anti-partisan operations. They are not known to have participated in any tank-versus-tank engagements. The *Waffen-SS Grenadier Brigade* is known to have lost two P 40s to British anti-tank fire while withdrawing from Italy into Austria. At least three P 40s were in RSI (Italian Social Republic) service in April of 1945. The Co-Belligerent *Regio Esercito* recovered several P 40s after Germany surrendered on 8 May 1945. Ansaldo-Fossati had 18 P 40s in various stages of construction when the war ended, but they were scrapped soon after the conflict.

One P 40 confiscated by the Germans was stored at the Kummersdorf test and evaluation ground in Eastern Germany. It and other vehicles stored at Kummersdorf – a PzKpfw VI Tiger II, two M4 Shermans, a *Jadgpanzer* VI *Jagdtiger* – were formed into a company that engaged Soviet armored forces in early April of 1945.

Lacking detailed reports on the P 40's combat performance, it is difficult to establish how it performed. We might compare the P 40 to its contemporary, the American M4 Sherman. Both tanks had identical armor, ground pressure, and speed. Their main guns had the same hitting power, but the Sherman possessed a larger ammunition capacity of 95 rounds versus the P 40's 65 rounds.

The only P 40 in running order is currently displayed at the Lecce Cavalry School in Southern Italy. Its original SPA engine was removed for separate display and replaced by a modern 190 HP diesel. This gives the P 40 the same performance standard as the 1960s Leopard 1 tank. Another P 40 – lacking an engine and employed by the Germans in a static fortification on the Gustav Line – is exhibited in the Rome Museum. (The Gustav Line was a series of German defenses stretched across Central Italy – southeast of Rome – from October of 1943 to May of 1944.)

Both Italy and Mussolini placed their armored forces' future on this heavy tank. Unable to match Allied production, they placed their fortunes on a technically superior design. The P 40 could have affected the tide of the war for Italy had it been produced in numbers in 1941 or 1942. The reason it didn't was due to the research and design problems, plus the excessive time from conception to finished product. Lacking operational heavy tanks to meet the increasing number of newer and heavier British and American tanks, Italian armored forces were doomed to defeat in North Africa. Even with the long research and

The P 40 pilot vehicle is parked outside Ansaldo-Fossati's Genoa plant in July of 1942. Production vehicles had a different engine deck and turret top from that on this prototype. Slanted turret and hull sides showed the influence of the Soviet T-34 tank on the P-40's design. Two aft-opening hatches were mounted on the turret roof.

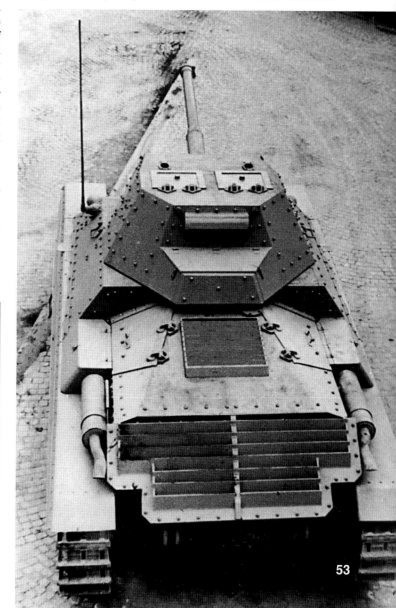

Fiat-Ansaldo *Carro Armato* P 40 Heavy Tank

Length:..............................5.8 M (19 feet 0.4 inch)
Width:................................2.8 M (9 feet 2.2 inches)
Height:...............................2.5 M (8 feet 2.4 inches)
Combat Weight:................26,430 KG (58,267 pounds)
Armor Thickness:.............14MM to 50MM
Powerplant:.......................One 330 HP SPA eight-cylinder, liquid-cooled, inline engine
Armament:.........................One 75MM Ansaldo L/34 gun with 65 rounds and one 8MM Breda Model 38 machine gun with 576 rounds in turret.
Maximum Speed:..............42 KMH (26 MPH)
Maximum Range:..............275 KM (171 miles)
Crew:..................................Four

A bracket for the 8MM Breda Model 38 machine gun is mounted on the P 40 turret's roof. This bracket is located immediately forward of the access hatch. Two semi-circular fittings on the turret roof protected the periscopes. The P 40 was armed with a 75MM Ansaldo L/34 gun, whose barrel protrudes from the turret front. This gun had a 34-caliber (2550MM; 100.4 inch) long barrel. The L/34 had a muzzle velocity of 610 M (2001 feet) per second and an effective range of 12,000 M (13,123 yards).

design period, Italy had no heavy tanks to face the Allied invasion of her homeland in 1943. By the time the P 40s were in service, the *Duce* was no longer in power and Italy sued for peace with the Allies. German forces occupying much of Italy used small quantities of P 40s until the conflict ended in May of 1945. This was an inglorious end to an excellent tank that represented the ultimate Italian tank design in World War Two.

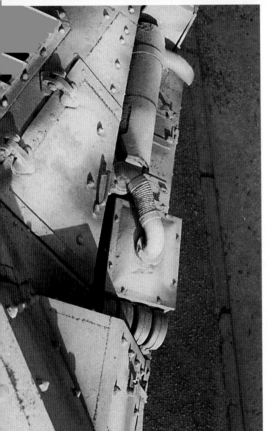

(Left) An oil filter is mounted on both the left and right engine deck sides. Each filter is located beside an engine inspection door. Both the shovel and the track connecting tool normally mounted on the fender were removed from this P-40.

(Above) A grill on the forward engine deck was an air intake for the engine compartment. P 40s were powered by a 330 HP SPA 8V 12-cylinder, liquid-cooled, inline diesel engine. Engine inspection doors flank this grill.

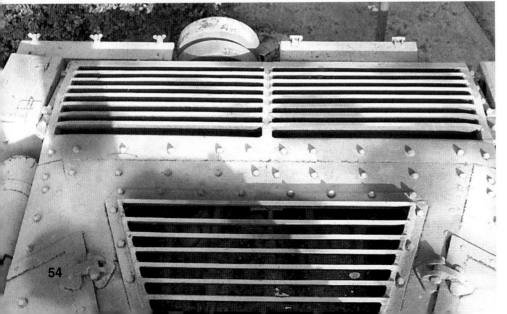

Additional grills were mounted on the P 40's aft engine deck. These grills – aft of the engine air intake grill – vented heated air from the engine compartment. A smoke discharge box is located right of the spare road wheel. A spare road wheel is mounted on the left rear hull, but the jack was removed on this vehicle.

Armored Cars

At the outbreak of World War Two, the *Regio Esercito* (Royal Italian Army) possessed a few dozen vintage armored car variants of varying quality and capability. Fiat began development of a new armored car during the late 1930s. After trials and a series of modifications, the new vehicle was adopted in March of 1940 and designated the *Autoblindo* (Armored Car) AB 40. Initial deliveries began in March of 1941. The first vehicles, almost all with 20MM Breda Model 35 cannon saw action in September of 1941, when a *Polizia Africa Italiana* (PAI; Italian African Police) company and an experimental cavalry platoon were sent to North Africa.

The AB 40 was a four wheeled turreted vehicle armed with three 8MM Breda Model 38 machine guns. This vehicle was powered by an 88 HP SPA six-cylinder gasoline engine mounted in the rear. The engine provided power to all four wheels. The transmission was equipped with six forward and two reverse speeds. A single spare wheel was mounted low on each side of the hull and allowed to revolve freely. This helped to prevent the hull center from grounding on uneven terrain. The AB 40's top speed was 76 KMH (47 MPH). The AB 40 was considered a fast and mobile vehicle both on road and cross-country. The hull armor consisted of 6MM to 15MM thick plates bolted to a steel frame.

AB 40s had both front and rear driving positions. This was a common feature for many armored cars of the day and one that allowed them to get out of trouble without taking the time to turn if they were in a restricted space. The primary driving position was over the front axle, which provided a larger field of vision for the driver. Primary crew access consisted of a pair of two-part, vertically hinged doors set into the hull sides behind the spare wheels. A single 8MM Breda Model 38 machine gun was ball mounted in the upper hull rear plate.

Two 8MM Breda Model 38s were mounted in a fully revolving armored polygonal turret. The turret armor consisted of 6MM to 18MM thick plates bolted together over a steel frame. The turret face was further protected by a rounded 18MM thick mantlet. The weapons were sighted using both a telescope and roof mounted periscope. The turret roof also incorporated a small hatch for the vehicle commander. A long range RF 3M radio was installed for communications, with its antenna mounted on the left side of the upper hull plate.

Wartime experience soon dictated an increase in firepower. A new turret design similar to that on the L 6-40 light tank was selected, which held a 20MM Breda Model 35 cannon with a co-axial 8MM Breda Model 38 machine gun. Two of the four turret ventilation cowls were retained on the forward side plates, while an added rear door allowed the gun to be removed. Two view slits were added in the left and right turret plates. A counterweight was later added to the turret rear. View slits and pistol ports were also added to the hull doors. The up-gunned vehicles were re-designated AB 41.

Overall, the AB 40/41 was well thought out and had several interesting features. There were some examples of poor detail design: difficult

An Ansaldo Lancia 1 ZM 4 x 2 armored car drives over the Libyan Desert in the Summer of 1942. The *Regio Esercito* employed several of these 1915-17 vintage vehicles for internal security at the outbreak of World War Two, particularly in Libya and Italian East Africa. This 1 ZM was armed with two 7.7MM Breda-SAFAT machine guns in the turret and one 8MM Breda Model 38 machine gun in the aft hull. Bands around the turret were (from top) red, white, and green.

Armored Car Unit Organization

AB 40/41 armored cars were issued to both *Bersaglieri* (light infantry) and cavalry units. They were organized in battalions (or groups for cavalry) of 40 cars and companies (or squadrons) of 17 vehicles. The organization was along the same lines as for the tank units. Alternately, these armored car groups/battalions were equipped with 28 L 6/40 light tanks per company or squadron.

Reconnaissance units and anti-tank infantry battalions were equipped with small detachments of *Semoventi da 47/32* on L 6/40 chassis or *Semoventi da 75/32* on M tank chassis.

The Italians deployed ten Fiat 611 6x4 armored cars to East Africa (Ethiopia, Eritrea, and Italian Somaliland) by 1940. Five of these vehicles were armed with a 37MM Vickers-Terni L/40 gun in a turret, with a rear-facing 6.5MM Breda Model 30 machine gun mounted in the hull. The Fiat 611 was a dual-drive vehicle, which could be fitted with tracks over the rear double wheels for greater off-road mobility.

The five remaining Fiat 611s sent to Italian East Africa were armed with three 6.5MM Breda Model 30 machine guns: two in the turret and one in the rear hull. Its 6MM to 15MM armor was vulnerable to armor-piercing rounds from the British .55 caliber (14MM) Boys anti-tank rifle.

power plant access, an unprotected fuel tank, one man turret, exposed traverse gear, uncomfortable rear gun mount, and lack of an interior bulkhead separating the engine and crew compartments. Nevertheless, the AB 40/41 was considered a good vehicle and one of the best of its kind.

AB 40/41s were issued to cavalry and *Bersaglieri* units and fought on all fronts. They proved highly suitable for reconnaissance, security, and escort duties. Desert (AB 42), anti-tank, and command variants appeared in late 1942, but only the command car was accepted for service. An improved model, the AB 43, was equipped with a shorter, wider turret just before the Armistice of 3 September 1943. It was armed with either the standard 20MM cannon in the lower AB 42 turret or the 47MM 47/40 tank gun in a welded and still wider turret. The hull machine gun was dispensed with in the latter version. AB 43 production was launched for German and RSI use after the Armistice. This car featured a servo-brake, a support for an anti-aircraft machine gun, and a smoke candle dispenser to the rear. This vehicle could carry six externally mounted 20 L (5.3 gallon) fuel cans, as on late production AB 41s.

In 1939, Fiat proposed a new armored car to the *Regio Esercito*, which was based on a specification the War Ministry issued in 1937. This proposal resulted in the *Autoblindo* (Armored Car) Abm 1 prototype, which is crossing a stream near Turin, Italy – Fiat's home city. The vehicle is painted overall Sahara Sand, with red-brown and gray-green vertical stripes. A spare wheel was mounted on both the left and right hull sides.

The *Regio Esercito* requested several changes in the Abm 1 prototype after early trials, resulting in the production AB 40 armored car. These modifications included a redesigned front hull, recessed headlights with armored covers, improved engine ventilation, flat fenders, and new cast steel spoked wheels. This vehicle was armed with three 8MM Breda Model 38 machine guns: two mounted in the turret, and a third, rear-firing gun in the hull. The AB 40 was powered by an 88 HP Fiat SPA engine and reached a maximum speed of 76 KMH (47 MPH).

Fiat developed the AB 40 into the AB 41 armored car in 1941. This vehicle was armed with a 20MM Breda Model 35 cannon and a co-axial 8MM Breda Model 38 machine gun in the turret. Sand filters and larger 'Libya' tires were installed for use in the desert. The RF 3M radio's antenna was hinged to lay aft when traveling under low bridges. The AB 41's 120 HP Fiat SPA engine gave it a maximum speed of 78 KMH (48 MPH).

(Above) Two *Bersaglieri* (light infantry) attempt to extricate an AB 41 from a North African sand dune. Italian armored cars were extensively modified for desert conditions; however, sand dunes remained difficult obstacles for these vehicles.

(Right) Nine AB 41s and an AB 40 – all assigned to a *Polizia Africa Italiana* (PAI; Italian African Police) company – are lined up in Libya. The PAI was the first organization to widely employ these armored cars in the Desert War. Cavalry and *Bersaglieri* reconnaissance units later used AB 40s and 41s against Allied forces in North Africa.

A PAI mechanic repairs the engine of an AB 40 or 41. The vehicle's powerplant and other systems required constant maintenance. The individual vehicle number 4 is painted on the left rear fender, while the white registration plate had *POLIZIA AFRICA ITALIANA* in blue above the number 0504 in black.

Cooling fans for the AB 40 or 41's SPA engine are exposed while two mechanics overhaul this vehicle in North Africa. A jack supports the right rear suspension components while both the wheel and tire were removed. *Regio Esercito* armored cars deployed to North Africa were normally painted overall Saharian Khaki.

A mechanic repairs the left front wheel removed from an AB 41, while its tire rests beside the mechanic. Two other soldiers work on the AB 41's 120 HP Fiat SPA engine. The *Regia Esercito* assigned motorized workshops to armored car units. These workshops kept these vehicles in running order in even the most difficult climates. An 8MM Breda Model 38 machine gun is mounted atop the turret for anti-aircraft use.

(Below Left) The Italians found armored cars highly useful in controlling occupied territories. Two AB 41s assigned to a *Bersaglieri* unit patrol a town in Corsica in September of 1942. Tree branches draped on these vehicles provided some camouflage by partially breaking up the vehicle's outline. Both vehicles' commanders — each standing in the turret — wear the *Bersaglieri*'s black feathers in their leather helmets. These feathers were normally worn on wide brimmed black hats or steel helmets as a corps distinction. Alternately, these troops wore a crimson fez with a blue tassel instead of the gray-green field cap.

Fiat-Ansaldo *Autoblindo* AB 40 Armored Car

Length:	5.2 M (17 feet 0.7 inches)
Width:	1.9 M (6 feet 2.8 inches)
Height:	2.4 M (7 feet 10.5 inches)
Combat Weight:	6850 KG (15,101 pounds)
Armor Thickness:	8.5MM
Powerplant:	One 88 HP Fiat SPA six-cylinder, liquid-cooled, inline engine
Armament:	Two 8MM Breda Model 38 machine guns with 4008 rounds in turret
Maximum Speed:	76 KMH (47 MPH)
Maximum Range:	400 KM (249 miles)
Crew:	Four

Fiat-Ansaldo *Autoblindo* AB 41 Armored Car

Same as for the AB 40, except:

Combat Weight:	7400 KG (16,314 pounds)
Powerplant:	One 120 HP Fiat SPA six-cylinder, liquid-cooled, inline engine
Armament:	One 20MM Breda Model 35 cannon with 456 rounds and one 8MM Breda Model 1938 machine gun with 1992 rounds in turret
Maximum Speed:	78 KMH (48 MPH)

Two AB 41s assigned to a Squadron of the 13th *Monferrato* Cavalry Regiment lead a convoy into Gafsa, Tunisia in February of 1943. The first armored car had the registration plate RₒEₜₒ 627 B on the front hull. Each AB 41 was crewed by a commander/gunner in the turret, two drivers (fore and aft), and a rear hull gunner. While the front driver is 'buttoned up' inside the hull, the other three crewmen lean out of the lead vehicle.

This AB 41 in North Africa was equipped with a lengthened radio antenna for improved communications in the desert. A 20 L (5.3 gallon) fuel can was mounted on the left rear fender, while ammunition boxes were placed on the engine deck. These provided an 'insurance policy' for the vehicle against the supply difficulties in the desert.

Two *Bersaglieri* crewmen service an AB 41 in North Africa. A camouflage net is draped over this overall gray-green vehicle. An 8MM Breda Model 38 machine gun is mounted on a pinnate atop the turret for anti-aircraft use. The rectangular marking for a 1st Platoon vehicle is painted on the turret side. Both the upper and lower left hull hatches are opened.

Three AB 41s lie abandoned in the North African desert after their destruction late in the desert campaign. Nearly all Allied armor-piercing projectiles penetrated the armored cars' 9MM thick armor. After the British victory at El Alamein, Egypt in October of 1942, German and Italian forces were pushed west across North Africa into Tunisia. The Axis troops faced British forces coming from the east and Anglo-American forces advancing from Morocco and Algeria.

Bersaglieri Cap Badge

(Gold wire for officers, warrant officers, and non-commissioned officers; brass or black thread for other ranks)

Regimental number (7 in this example) at center of badge.

The AB 43 was the last *Autoblindo* that Fiat developed during World War Two. This vehicle featured several improvements, including a 110 HP Ansaldo engine and 14MM thick armor. A new, lower turret mounted either a 47MM 47/40 gun (in this example) or a 20MM Breda Model 35 cannon. Two 8MM Breda Model 38 machine guns were mounted in the hull. Additional 20 L fuel 'jerrycans' are strapped to the front fenders and hull sides.

The Italians converted several AB 41s (including this example) and earlier AB 40s into *Ferroviarie* (Railway) vehicles from 1942. Wheels mounted on the hull sides allowed this vehicle to ride on railroad track. The *Regio Esercito* deployed these AB 40/41 *Ferroviarie* cars to the Balkans for anti-partisan patrols.

Fiat-Ansaldo *Autoblindo* AB 43 Armored Car

Length:...................5.3 м (17 feet 4.7 inches)
Width:....................1.9 м (6 feet 2.8 inches)
Height:...................2.5 м (8 feet 2.4 inches)
Combat Weight:....7970 кг (17,571 pounds)
Armor Thickness:.6мм to 22мм
Powerplant:...........One 110 нр Ansaldo engine
Armament:............One 47мм 47/40 gun with 63
                        rounds in turret and two
                        8мм Breda Model 38
                        machine guns with 648
                        rounds in hull.
Maximum Speed:..88 кмн (55 мрн)
Maximum Range:..535 км (332 miles)
Crew:.....................Four

A 20мм turret-mounted cannon is mounted on this factory-fresh AB 43. This vehicle is painted in the 1944-45 Ansaldo scheme, which consisted of red-brown and gray-green patches separated by thin sand streaks. German forces used the AB 43 – redesignated the *Pz Spähwagen AB 43 203 (i)* – after the Italian Armistice in 1943 until the conflict ended. Italian police units employed AB 43s after World War Two.

Armored Personnel Carriers and *Lince* Scout Car

A light Armored Personnel Carrier (APC), based on the chassis of the Saharian 37 four-wheel drive tractor, was designed in the Spring of 1941. The vehicle was designed to carry eight troops, protected by 8мм thick armor, and equipped with a single 8мм Breda Model 38 machine gun. The Saharian-based APC was not considered successful due to a lack of vision slits and firing ports. A small number were completed in 1942, but these were not issued to armored units. The vehicles were assigned to escort duties.

Fiat developed a larger and more cumbersome 9 мт (9.9 ton) APC in late 1942. This vehicle employed the chassis and running gear of the diesel powered 665NM four-wheel drive truck and was extensively armored. The APC was equipped with side and rear firing ports and capable of carrying 29 troops and a crew of two. This vehicle was also envisioned for the armored divisions in Africa, but the *Regio Esercito* preferred to use it in the occupied territories for anti-partisan duties.

The Italians developed a third, all-wheel drive armored vehicle in 1942. The vehicle, known as the *Lince* (Lynx) scout car, was similar to the popular British Daimler Dingo armored car, some of which had been captured in Libya in 1941. The *Lince* was tested in early 1943 and standardized in February of that year.

The hull was made of 8мм to 14мм welded armor plate, joined to a rigid chassis with independent suspension and all-wheel steering. An order was placed for 330 vehicles, which differed from the British Dingo only in the engine – a 60 нр Lancia – and having an 8мм Breda Model 38 machine gun on a ball mount in the left front superstructure. One out of three or four cars mounted an RF 2 CA radio set. The *Lince* vehicles were issued to reconnaissance and liaison squadrons within the armored/motorized divisions and reconnaissance groups.

A considerable number of *Lince* vehicles were produced for the German and RSI (*Repubblica Sociale Italiana*; Italian Social Republic) units until late 1944, and several survive in museums and private collections today.

The Italians – like the Germans and Soviets – employed armored railroad cars during World War Two. The *Genio Ferrovieri* (Railroad Engineer Corps) operated 16 Fiat-Ansaldo LIBLI (*Littorina Blindata*; Armored Rail Car) diesel-powered vehicles. They were employed on anti-partisan security duties in Italian-occupied Yugoslavia. Each LIBLI was armed with two turret-mounted 47мм guns atop the car. This vehicle was also equipped with six 8мм Breda Model 38 machine guns, two Model 40 flame-thrower, and either two 45мм mortars or one 20мм cannon.

Fiat-Ansaldo produced 16 examples of the LIBLI (*Littorina Blindata*; Armored Rail Car) for the *Regio Esercito*'s Engineer Corps prior to the Armistice. This was the first vehicle, which was delivered in September of 1942. The LIBLI were deployed to the Axis-occupied Balkans from late 1942 until 1944. Two 115 HP diesel engines drove the 13.6 M (44 foot 7.4 inch) long vehicle to a maximum speed of 118 KMH (73 MPH). Each car had two M 13-40 turrets, each with one 47MM Ansaldo 47/32 gun. Additional armament included two 45MM Brixia mortars – later replaced by one 20MM Breda Model 38 cannon – six 8MM Breda Model 38 machine guns, and two Model 40 flame-throwers. Armor thickness ranged from 6MM in the first eight cars to 11.5MM in the last eight vehicles. Each LIBLI had a crew of 18 to 23 men, which included a radio operator for the RF 3M set and the commanding officer.

The *Regio Esercito* was impressed by the success of the British Army's Long Range Desert Groups (LRDGs) in North Africa. These units successfully raided Axis communications and airfields. Italy's reply to the LRDGs was the *Camionetta desertica mod. 42* (Desert Van Model 42), which entered production in July of 1942. This vehicle had a modified AB 41 chassis with an unarmored hull. Ten 20 L fuel cans were mounted on racks along each side, with four more 'jerrycans' placed on the front fenders. The *Camionetta deserti-ca mod. 42* (also called the *Camionetta AS 42 Sahariana*) was 5.8 M (19 feet 0.3 inches) long, 2.2 M (7 feet 2.6 inches) wide, and 1.9 M (6 feet 2.8 inches) high. It had a maximum weight of 4000 KG (8818 pounds) and was powered by an 80 HP Fiat SPA engine. The *Camionetta* had a maximum speed of 90 KMH (56 MPH) and a maximum range of 800 KM (497 miles). It was crewed by two or three men.

This *Camionetta desertica mod. 42* was armed with one 20MM *Fucile anticarro* (Solothurn S18-1100) anti-tank rifle on a pintel mount in the front right fighting compartment area. The *Fucile anticarro* had a muzzle velocity of 910 M (2986 feet) per second, a firing rate of 15 to 20 rounds per minute, and could penetrate up to 40MM of armor at 100 M (109 yards). Either a 20MM Breda Model 35 cannon or a 47MM Breda 47/32 gun replaced the Solothurn weapon. An 8MM Breda Model 38 machine gun was fitted immediately aft of the windshield. *Camionetta desertica mod. 42* reconnaissance vehicles could carry up to three Breda Model 38s, plus a tripod for firing the machine gun from the ground.

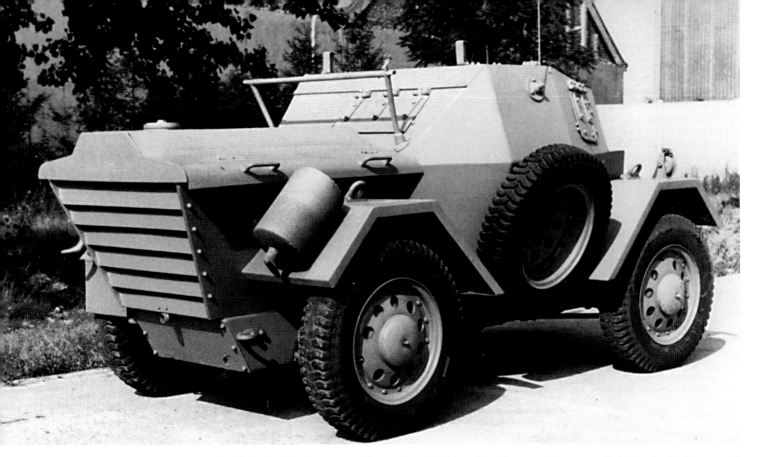

(Below) The *Lince*'s driver sat to the right, beside the commander. This driver's position gave him a good field of vision ahead of, to the sides, and aft of the vehicle. A square viewing hatch was mounted on the right side wall.

Lancia's *Lince* (Lynx) armored car was a light 4 x 4 vehicle powered by a 60 HP Lancia gasoline engine. Although a copy of British Daimler Dingo Mk IA, the *Lince* had a different engine deck and rear louvers from the British vehicle. This was done to accommodate the Lancia engine, which had a different configuration from the Dingo's powerplant. The *Lince* had a maximum speed of 86 KMH (53 MPH) and a maximum range of 200 KM (124 miles).

Lancia *Lince Autoblinda* Armored Car

Length:.................3.2 M (10 feet 6 inches)
Width:...................1.8 M (5 feet 10.9 inches)
Height:..................1.7 M (5 feet 6.9 inches)
Combat Weight:....3140 KG (6922 pounds)
Armor Thickness:.6MM to 30MM
Powerplant:..........One 70 HP Lancia liquid-cooled, inline engine
Armament:............One 8MM Breda Model 38 machine gun in hull
Maximum Speed:..86 KMH (53 MPH)
Maximum Range:..400 KM (249 miles)
Crew:....................Two

Production *Lince* armored cars were armed with an 8MM Breda Model 38 machine gun. This weapon was located on a ball-mount located on the front left superstructure. An RF 1 CA radio was mounted inside the hull for the commander's use. Each *Lince* had a two-man crew: a commander/gunner and a driver.

The *Carro Protetto* (Protected Car) AS 37 Armored Personnel Carrier (APC) entered production in 1941. This vehicle was based on the Fiat/SPA TL 37 support vehicle for North African operations and had 8MM armor plating. Seven infantrymen were accommodated behind

Fiat/SPA *Autocarro Protetto* AS 37 Armored Personnel Carrier

Length:..................5 M (16 feet 4.8 inches)
Width:....................1.9 M (6 feet 2.8 inches)
Height:..................1.8 M (5 feet 10.9 inches)
Combat Weight:....5600 KG (12,346 pounds)
Armor Thickness:.8.5MM
Powerplant:............One 70 HP SPA 4-cylinder, liquid-cooled, inline engine
Armament:.............One 8MM Breda Model 38 machine gun in troop compartment
Maximum Speed:..50 KMH (31 MPH)
Maximum Range:..600 KM (373 miles)
Crew:....................Two; Seven troops in compartment

The Fiat 665NM *Scudato* (Shielded) was an APC developed in 1942. This vehicle was based on the Fiat 665NM truck and carried 29 infantrymen and a crew of two. Vision slots for the crew were mounted on the cab front and sides, while troops in the fighting compartment had ports for firing their guns from inside the vehicle.

the driver, but they could not fire from within the APC. It was armed with an 8MM Breda Model 38 machine gun on the hull roof, which exposed the gunner to enemy fire. A radio antenna was mounted on the left upper hull and was retracted from inside the vehicle.

The Fiat 665NM *Scudato*'s troop compartment was completely surrounded by light armor plate. Circular firing ports allowed the troops to fire their weapons while in the vehicle. Infantrymen entered the *Scudato* using a ladder mounted on the rear. The driver and commander entered their compartment through side doors. The *Regio Esercito* considered the 9 MT (9.9 ton) *Scudato* too cumbersome for front line service; instead, the approximately 100 vehicles built were employed on anti-partisan operations in the Balkans.

A *Semovente da 75/18* (RₒEₜₒ 6225) on an M 42 hull assigned to the 31st Tank Regiment is parked on an Italian street during 1943. This vehicle has red-brown and gray-green patches over the Saharian Khaki base. The white registration plate on the front hull has RₒEₜₒ (*Regio Esercito*; Royal Italian Army) and a flaming grenade in red, followed by the black number. (Bundesarchiv)

Italian Armored Camouflage

Two camouflage schemes were employed on Italian tanks during the late 1930s. One was red-brown (approximately FS30108) oversprayed with small gray-green (approximately FS34159) patches. In early 1939, large gray-green streaks were sprayed over the red-brown finish. Fiat-Ansaldo began using an overall dark sand color beginning in 1937. This was overpainted with thin streaks of brown and green on all prototypes used in presentations and shows, and on some export vehicles.

Regio Esercito headquarters in Tripoli, Libya proposed an overall *sabbia-kaki* (sand-khaki) vehicle scheme by the end of 1939. *Regia Aeronautica* (Royal Italian Air Force) vehicles in Libya already used this color. Nevertheless, soft-skinned motor vehicles and artillery based in the Italian colony maintained their original overall gray-green scheme

New M 13-40 tanks left the factory finished in the standard overall flat gray-green paint of other military vehicles. Such paint was not suitable for the desert war and some commanders tried a more convenient camouflage consisting of sharply defined areas of green and sand, overall dark ochre, and others. On 18 March 1941, the Army Staff ordered all war material sent to North Africa to be painted overall *kaki sahariano* (Saharian Khaki, approximately FS20260). Those vehicles already painted gray-green were often oversprayed with sand colored patches or another polychromatic scheme.

Other camouflage schemes (dark brown, sand, and green) were approved in 1942 for special fighting vehicles, including rail cars, and were extended to include all armored fighting vehicles after May of 1943. In the meantime, tanks, armored cars, and self propelled guns, were delivered painted in yellow sand with rounded green and brown patches. On 7 June 1943, an order was issued for overspraying the basic gray-green color with brown, green, and yellow patches or streaks; however, few vehicles were painted in these scheme before the Armistice of 3 September 1943.

Several armored vehicles remained in their sand color – sometimes up through 1945. Other vehicles – such as the M tanks, assault guns, and armored cars assigned to the *Ariete II* Armored Division in the first half of 1943 – still painted overall sand were oversprayed with irregular patches of gray-green. This often covered the registration plates and the white 70 CM (27.6 inch) diameter air identification disc on the turret roofs. Armored vehicles produced by Ansaldo during 1944-45 received an elaborate camouflage scheme of red-brown and gray-green patches separated by thinly sprayed sand streaks.

Vehicle Identification Plates

Tanks wore a white registration plate consisting of the letters RₒEₜₒ (*Regio Esercito*; Royal Italian Army) in red, a red flaming grenade, and the serial number in black. After 1940, the superscript letters were underlined thusly: RₒEₜₒ. Rear tank plates – 230 CM x 150 CM (90.6 inches by 59.1 inches) – were made of enameled stamped iron sheet and fixed to the lower left rear of the vehicle. The same identification system was painted on the center of the front plate beginning in March of 1941. The smaller L 6-40 light tank had the front identification plate divided into two parts, which were separated by the towing eye.

The armored cars displayed a similar plate, but this lacked the grenade device and had a small red B (*Blindo*; Car) at the end of the black vehicle number. Remaining vehicle types had no particular emblem; only the red R.E. and black number. Trailers were identified with the same lettering and a red R (*Rimorchio*; Trailer) after the black number. A capital R was used on trailers with two or more axles, while a lower case r identified one-axle trailers.

Armored cars assigned to the *Polizia Africa Italiana* (PAI; Italian Africa Police) used different markings and number plates. These early plates had *POLIZIA AFRICA ITALIANA* in blue letters followed by the vehicle number in black. From October of 1939, these plates had PAI in red, followed by black numbers. Armored cars in Libya did not change their plates until 1942. Green, white, and red Italian flags and large black individual numbers were painted on the hull to aid in recognition.

The vehicle number plate was not the same as the chassis and engine numbers for M and P tanks. For example, the M 14-41 displayed at the Aberdeen Proving Ground, Maryland wears the vehicle plate RₒEₜₒ 3521, while the hull number 735 is stamped in 1 CM (0.4 inch) high numbers on the front tow ring. The engine number 100036 is located on the top front. This tank was built in the Summer of 1941 and was assigned to the 133rd *Littorio* Armored Division. Its RF 1 CA radio equipment was given the number 0480.

Front Plate (Typical)
(Front Plate painted on vehicle, while rear plate was screwed to vehicle.)

Rear Plate (Typical)